Ivory-billed Woodpeckers

THE
IVORY-BILLED
WOODPECKER

by James T. Tanner

Dover Publications, Inc., New York

Published in Canada by General Publishing Company, Ltd., 30 Lesmill Road, Don Mills, Toronto, Ontario.

Published in the United Kingdom by Constable and Company, Ltd., 10 Orange Street, London W.C. 2.

This Dover edition, first published in 1966, is an unabridged and unaltered republication of the work originally published in 1942 as Research Report Number 1 of the National Audubon Society.

In the 1942 edition the frontispiece was reproduced in color, but is here reproduced as a black-and-white halftone.

This edition is published by special arrangement with the National Audubon Society.

Library of Congress Catalog Card Number: 66-19045

Manufactured in the United States of America
Dover Publications, Inc.
180 Varick Street
New York, N.Y. 10014

FOREWORD

THE National Audubon Society considers facts obtainable through scientific research the essential basis for wise policies governing the conservation of wild-life resources.

The Ivory-billed Woodpecker is the rarest North American bird. Efforts to conserve and restore it must be of prompt application, as the factors undermining its survival continue to develop with increasing tempo. The present world-wide war, with its pressure for maximum lumber production, underscores the predicament of the Ivory-bills.

That the Ivory-bill shall not, as a part of America's natural heritage, go the way of the Passenger Pigeon and the Great Auk, is an objective of the National Audubon Society.

A way was found by the Society to sponsor and finance field research in tune with its rather slender available resources. This involves the coöperation of universities and is known as the Audubon Research Fellowship Plan. Through the good offices of Dr. Arthur A. Allen, we were very fortunate indeed in enlisting the coöperation of Cornell University in making this plan applicable to the problem of how to conserve the Ivory-billed Woodpecker.

Dr. Allen and his associates were already deeply interested, and he generously undertook to plan and supervise the research work and select as Audubon Fellow the man he felt best qualified. The choice of James T. Tanner was a happy one.

New York, N.Y.
September 15, 1942

JOHN H. BAKER
Executive Director
National Audubon Society

I

PREFACE

THE greatest tragedy in nature is the extinction of a species. We may condone reasonable control of carnivorous animals in those parts of their range taken over by human settlement. We may even understand the commercialization of the Passenger Pigeon by interests which regarded them only as an inexhaustible supply of 'food on the wing.' But where is the man who knowingly would stand by and watch a marvelous creation of nature—harmless to man's interests, and of no intrinsic commercial value—be forced into the vortex of extirpation without even raising his voice in protest? Surely no intelligent human being could be indifferent to the passing of the last Ivory-billed Woodpecker, and certainly no philanthropic organization dedicated to the conservation of wildlife could let this come about without making some effort to prevent it.

But what can one do to save a species when the facts necessary for a correct diagnosis of its troubles are not available? The literature of ornithology is replete with records of the past occurrence of the bird over quite an extensive range in southeastern United States. There are plenty of skins and even a few skeletons in the museums of the country, and there are a few published observations on the nesting and feeding habits of the bird but there is little to indicate why the magnificent Ivory-bill should not be able to persist as well as its smaller relative the Pileated Woodpecker.

For years it has been obvious that an intensive study of the bird in its natural haunts would be essential to determine its needs before any constructive work for its preservation could be attempted. Because of the nature and remoteness of the Ivory-bill's habitat the problem offered such difficulties as to make it prohibitive to most ornithologists who have professional obligations of one sort or another. And yet obviously it offered a full-time job for a well-trained student of birds who could devote his entire time to it over a period of years. Fortunately we have such persons among the graduate students in our universities.

When the National Audubon Society decided that such a study should be made, Mr. Baker invited me to lend such aid as I could toward setting up in the Graduate School of Cornell University an Audubon Fellowship and selecting the student who should perform the arduous labors involved. The Graduate School was receptive to the proposal because, in previous years, many of the graduate students in the Laboratory of Ornithology had produced life-history reports of considerable value and it so happened that we had just the right man available for the task.

The Cornell-American Museum Expedition for recording the voices of vanishing birds had just returned, after rediscovering the Ivory-bill in Louisiana, and on this expedition we had taken with us as student helper, James Tanner of Cortland, New York, recently graduated from Cornell with honors in ornithology and biology. On this trip he had proved that he had the qualities necessary for a field ornithologist: an ability to rough it and to get along with all kinds of people in all kinds of situations, a natural adaptability, ingenuity, initiative, originality, and a willingness to work. Above all, he had shown a clear mind and superior intelligence. Moreover he had, with us, enjoyed the thrill of the search and the final discovery of two Ivory-billed Woodpeckers' nests and he had spent many days observing the birds. That the selection of James Tanner for the Audubon Ivory-billed Woodpecker Fellowship was a wise choice is indicated by the accompanying report—the

III

results of three seasons' intensive field work and a great deal of clear but conservative thinking. It does not tell how the Ivory-billed Woodpeckers can be saved by the expenditure of words alone. Much real work must be done—virgin forest must be set aside as a sanctuary and intelligent management practices applied. Is the bird worth it? Is the preservation of a glorious species that has taken millions of years to evolve worth ten dollars? Is it worth ten million dollars?

Today we are measuring our love of freedom in billions of dollars and thousands of lives. The American way of living is worth anything we have to pay to preserve it, and the Ivory-billed Woodpecker is one little guide post on our way of life, a reminder of that pioneering spirit that has made us what we are, a people rich in resourcefulness and powerful to accomplish what is right. The Ivory-bill is a product of the great force of evolution acting on American bird life in ages past, to produce in our southeastern United States the noblest woodpecker of them all—one that inspired Mark Catesby and John James Audubon and Alexander Wilson—one that has lured scores of recent ornithologists to the cypress jungles of South Carolina, Florida, and Louisiana in the ardent hope of but seeing one individual alive. Is it worth ten dollars to save it? Is it worth ten million dollars? It is worth whatever we must pay to preserve it before it is too late. I commend this report to you as the best working hypothesis we have for the possible preservation of this species that is balanced on the rim of extinction.

Ithaca, N.Y.
August 1, 1942

ARTHUR A. ALLEN
Professor of Ornithology
Cornell University

ACKNOWLEDGMENTS

During the research on the Ivory-billed Woodpecker I received much help and wise advice from Professor Arthur A. Allen, Cornell University, who supervised the project, and who gave many suggestions on the preparation of my doctoral thesis, which was the basis for this present report. I wish to express my indebtedness to him at this time. Likewise I acknowledge with appreciation the assistance received from members of the staff of the National Audubon Society, especially John H. Baker, the Executive Director, who has given many helpful suggestions during the research work and on the preparation of this report for publication. I acknowledge also the help of Mrs. Margaret Brooks Hickey, who carefully edited the entire manuscript and managed the printing of the report.

The New York Zoological Society very kindly permitted the use of the four-color plates of Dr. George Miksch Sutton's painting of the Ivory-billed Woodpecker for the frontispiece. Plates 1, 9 and 16 are from photographs taken by Professor Arthur A. Allen, and I am thankful to him for their use, also to Roger Tory Peterson for his work on some of the maps.

It would be impossible to name at this time all the people who assisted the work in the field. But I do wish to acknowledge the help of J. J. Kuhn of Tallulah, Louisiana, who for two seasons in the forest of the Singer Tract helped me in finding and studying the Ivory-bills there. I am also indebted to the Louisiana Department of Conservation and its officials for aid in carrying on the work in the Singer Tract. To all the others, representatives of the United States Fish and Wildlife Service, conservation officials and wardens of the different states, museum curators, logging men, hunters and other woodsmen, I can only in this way express my gratitude.

JAMES T. TANNER

New York, N. Y.
September 15, 1942

TABLE OF CONTENTS

APPENDIX

LIST OF ILLUSTRATIONS

PLATES

FIGURES

INTRODUCTION

THE Ivory-billed Woodpecker is the largest woodpecker in North America and the second largest in the world, being exceeded in size only by the Imperial Woodpecker of Mexico. It originally lived in the bottomlands and swampy forests of the coastal plain from southeastern North Carolina around to eastern Texas and northward in the lower swamps of the Mississippi valley as far as southern Illinois and eastern Oklahoma.

The Ivory-bill attracted attention early in the annals of American natural history. Its large size, striking coloration, ivory-white bill, and curious voice have impressed nearly everyone who has seen it, from the earliest observers to the few woodsmen and naturalists who have seen Ivory-bills today. Catesby, the first to describe and illustrate the species, was impressed by the bird; Audubon (1831) nicknamed the Ivory-bill "Van Dyke," because of the pleasing contrast of its ebony, white, and scarlet plumage, and mentioned the bird many times in his writings. Likewise, modern naturalists and simple woodsmen who have seen Ivory-bills, and I myself, have been impressed by the bird's striking and graceful appearance and the energy and strength of its actions and attitudes.

The interest of naturalists in the Ivory-bill was increased because of the bird's comparative scarcity, and because they early realized that its numbers were decreasing and its range becoming smaller. Hasbrouck in 1891 stated that the distribution of the Ivory-bill was restricted at that early date to the larger swamps of the lower and southerly part of its original range. Laws protecting the bird from shooting and from egg collectors were passed, but that did not halt its decrease. Several possible causes for the Ivory-bill's disappearance were advanced; the one most frequently suggested was that this bird of wild and solitary haunts could not stand the presence of mankind or association with advancing civilization. For a few years after 1926 many reputable naturalists considered the Ivory-bill to be extinct, as none knew of any living birds, but in 1932 a few individuals were found still existing in Louisiana, and later a few in South Carolina.

Discovery that the Ivory-billed Woodpecker was not yet extinct aroused hope for its preservation and in 1937 the National Audubon Society established a research fellowship for the study of the Ivory-bill. It was on this fellowship that the studies were carried on which are described in this report.

The primary aim of the investigation was to discover the necessary facts for planning an effective conservation program for the Ivory-billed Woodpecker. This included determining the present distribution and numbers of the Ivory-bills, and studying its ecology and life history to learn the factors which limit the existence of the species, and especially those which can be controlled by man.

Much of this work had to be done in the range and haunts of the bird, and therefore extended trips were taken throughout the South to investigate areas from which Ivory-bills had been reported, to search for new areas, and to examine the localities where the birds once lived. Altogether I investigated at least forty-five different areas, and in doing so traveled about 45,000 miles by car and some by train, and uncounted miles by foot, boat, and horse. The times spent in the South on this field work were as follows: January 6 to July 25, 1937; December 1 to December 29, 1937; February 15 to August 24, 1938; November 21, 1938 to June 23, 1939; and November 28 to December 8, 1939—a total of about twenty-one months. Part of the time in the field was employed in analyzing the habitats and in studying the habits and behavior of the birds themselves, and part was spent in hunting for Ivory-bill locations to find the present numbers and distribution of the species. Detailed accounts of the methods used in hunting for the birds and in observing them and collecting data are included in some of the following sections.

In addition to the field work, ornithological literature and other sources were thoroughly explored, several museum collections were examined, and other ornithologists, collectors, and native guides were consulted at every opportunity. Since the primary aim of the investigation was to lay down a foundation of facts for a conservation or management program, I have tried to assemble as complete an account as possible of the ecology and life history of the species and to include every factor bearing on the survival of the bird.

The chief difficulty of the study has been that of drawing conclusions from relatively few observations, necessary because of the extreme scarcity of the bird. My own observations of the birds have been entirely confined to a few individuals in one part of Louisiana, and although these observations covered a large percentage of all the Ivory-bills living in the country, the conclusions drawn from them will not necessarily apply to the species as it once was nor to individuals living in other areas. The difficulty of finding the birds, even when their whereabouts was known, also limited the number of observations. Especially was this true in the non-breeding season. With these considerations in mind, one must draw conclusions carefully and with reservations.

Part I. The Ivory-billed Woodpecker

CHAPTER 1

General Description

THE Ivory-bill (Plate 1) is the largest North American woodpecker, averaging about twenty inches in length. The Southern Pileated is about seventeen inches long, but it is a stockier bird and the difference in length is not a reliable character unless the two species are seen together.

The plumage of the Ivory-bill is mainly a glossy black with purplish reflections. A white stripe starting on each cheek continues down each side of the neck to the back, where the two stripes curve together to meet in the middle of the back. The outer half of all the secondaries is white, as are the ends of the inner primaries; this makes a large white patch on the rear half of the wing, narrowing toward the tip. This white is conspicuous even when the bird folds its wings, appearing then as a large triangular patch on the lower back, like a white saddle.

The male has a prominent scarlet crest, while the crest of the female is entirely black.

The bill of the Ivory-bill is large and ivory-white. The general shape of the bird is long and slender, accentuated by the long and tapering tail.

The best field character for identifying the Ivory-bill is the large white patch on the wing that is visible on the back when the bird is perched. This patch can be seen for a long ways and looks the same in all lights; the only other bird with a similar marking is the much smaller and different Red-headed Woodpecker. The back of a Pileated Woodpecker at rest is a uniform slaty black, without white (see Fig. 1).

Many times Pileated Woodpeckers have been mistaken for Ivory-bills because of their light-colored bills, which vary from black to a light horn color. Also, the white cheek of a Pileated might be mistaken for white on the bill. The bill of a bird, even a large one, is hard to see at the top of a tree. The bill is thus not a good character for differentiating the two species in the field.

The manner of flight of the bird cannot be used as a reliable field character. Much has been written and said on how the Ivory-bill flies directly and straight while the Pileated's flight undulates, but I have frequently seen Pileateds fly directly, in no way different from the flight of the larger bird. In fact, both birds vary considerably in their manner of flight. Nor can the *amount* of white visible on the wing of a flying bird be used as a character, as the open wing of a Pileated shows as much white from beneath as does the wing of an Ivory-bill.

In flight the Ivory-bill looks surprisingly like a Pintail; its neck is long and slender, its tail long and tapering, and the wings rather narrow. The important field character is that the white on the wing is on the rear half. By comparison a Pileated is stocky with shorter wings, the tail is slightly forked, and the white is on the front half of the wing (see Fig. 2).

To summarize, the *position* of the white on the wing is by far the most reliable field character at all times. In the Ivory-bill the white is on the rear half of the wing and is visible on the back when the bird is perched and its wings folded. In the Pileated the white is on the front half of the wing and is hidden when its wings are folded.

The call of the Ivory-bill has been described by Audubon (1831) as a repeated *pait* resembling the high false note of a clarinet, and by Chapman (1932) as a repeated and nasal *yap* sounding like a tin trumpet. Both descriptions fit the call of an Ivory-bill. The call can be imitated fairly well by tooting on the mouthpiece of a clarinet or saxophone, although the resulting note lacks the slightly trumpet-like tone of the Ivory-bill. To my ear, the best spelling of the call is that used by Allen and Kellogg—a nasal *kent, kent*.

The Ivory-bill's call resembles very much the call of the Red-breasted Nuthatch, only of course much louder. The bird usually calls repeated single or double yaps—*kent, kent-kent, kent*. Another common call is a more prolonged, upward-slurring *kient—kient—kient*. More detailed de-

1

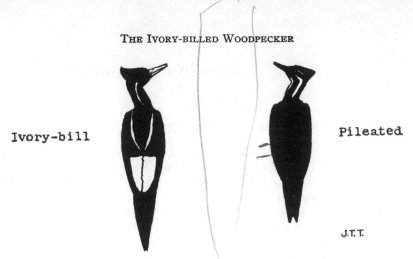

Ivory-bill   Pileated

J.T.T.

Fig. 1.   Ivory-billed and Pileated Woodpeckers, perched.

scriptions of the bird's notes and calls are given in a following section on general behavior.

There is little possibility of confusing the calls of the Ivory-bill and the Pileated; both the tone and the form of the two calls are different. The mating call of the Pileated has some resemblance to that of the Ivory-bill, but that is all. Once heard and recognized, the Ivory-bill's call is not easily confused with any other sound to be heard in the woods; it is a fine aid in identification.

Fig. 2.   Ivory-billed and Pileated Woodpeckers, flying, as seen from below.

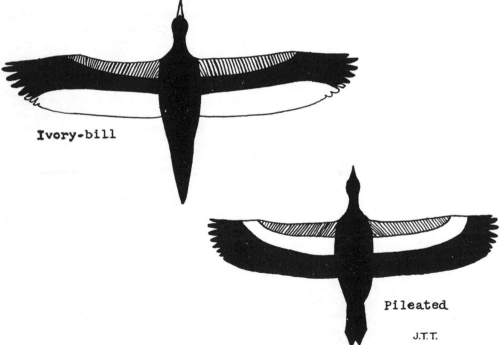

Ivory-bill

Pileated

J.T.T.

Part II.   Distribution and Habitat

CHAPTER 2

Original Distribution

THE maps, Figs. 3–11, showing the distribution of the Ivory-billed Woodpecker, indicate that the bird was originally confined, except for a few records, to the southeastern and lower Mississippi valley states. Within these regions it lived in swampy forests, especially the large bottomland river swamps of the coastal plain and Mississippi Delta, and the cypress swamps of Florida. It was most abundant in the lower bottoms of the Mississippi River and of the rivers in South Carolina and Georgia, and in Florida swamps. More Ivory-bill records and specimens have come from the state of Florida than from all the other states put together; this is partly due to the large number of collectors and observers that have worked in Florida, but it indicates that the Ivory-bill was probably more abundant and widespread in that region than elsewhere.

Many Ivory-bill reports have been based upon mistaken identifications of Pileated Woodpeckers. This has been more true at the edges of the Ivory-bill range than it has in the center, as observers in the former localities have had little or no chance to become familiar with the real Ivory-bill. Consequently it has been difficult and always uncertain to say what the limits of its range were, but the following statement of the original range of the Ivory-bill is what I believe most probably true after examining all available records.

Range of the Ivory-billed Woodpecker: southeastern, Gulf, and Mississippi valley states of the United States; north in the coastal plain to southeastern North Carolina; south in Florida to southern Florida; west through the Gulf states to the Brazos River in Texas; north along the larger rivers to west-central Alabama, southern Illinois, and southeastern Missouri; and west along the larger rivers to southeastern Oklahoma and northeastern Texas.

The following records can be considered as accidental or as mistaken and unproven identifications: Fort Macon, N.C. (Coues and Yarrow);

Franklin County in southeastern Indiana (Haymond); Fayette and Kansas City, Mo. (Cooke, 1888); Franklin County, Tenn. (Bendire); San Marco and Guadalupe Rivers, Tex. (J. M. H.); and New Braunfels, Tex. (Roemer).

The following series of maps plots more accurately the past distribution of the Ivory-billed Woodpecker, and also shows the distribution of the swamp areas within the range of the bird. The range of the Ivory-bill has been divided for mapping into eight regions—Carolina region, Georgia-northern Florida region, southern Florida region, Alabama region, lower Mississippi Delta, upper Mississippi Delta, Arkansas-Oklahoma region, and east Texas region. On the map of every region each Ivory-bill locality is spotted and numbered, and the correspondingly numbered key or legend accompanying each map gives the pertinent data for each location. Locations were plotted as accurately as possible using the data available.

Distribution of the swamp areas, shown outlined by dashed lines, has been plotted from forest type maps, vegetation maps, and soil maps as indicated in the legend accompanying each regional map. The numbered key to the locations gives the information in this order: location, date of record, observer or collector and, in parenthesis, the authority or source for the record. Names and dates in the parenthesis refer to the bibliography.

CAROLINA REGION

(Fig. 3)

1. 12 mi. north of Wilmington, N.C.; about 1800; Alexander Wilson (1811).
2. Cheraw, S.C.; Apr. 1876 (R. C. Murphy). Pee Dee River, near Cheraw; Apr. 1889; Dr. C. Kollock (A. T. Wayne, 1910).
3. Pine barrens of S.C.; about 1850; Burnett (1854).
4. Black Oak Id., Clarendon Co., S.C.; about 1930; W. M. Ridgill (verbal).

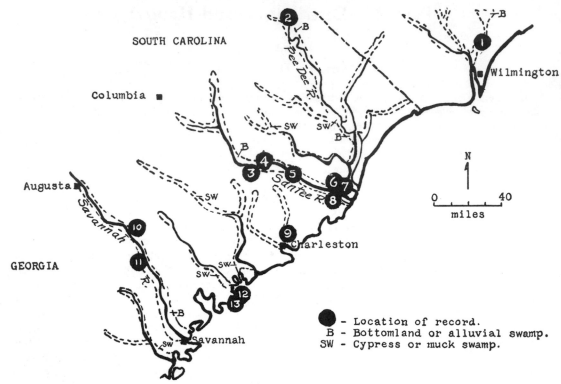

Fig. 3.   Ivory-billed Woodpecker distribution, Carolina region.

5. Santee swamp, near St. Stephens, S.C.; about 1925; Sam Platt (verbal).

6. Santee swamp, Georgetown Co., S.C.; 1935; Alexander Sprunt (epist.).

7. Santee swamp, Georgetown Co., S.C.; 1935–37; H. Shokes (verbal).

8. Santee swamp, lower Berkeley Co.; about 1930; Melamphy (records Nat. Audubon Soc.).

9. Cypress swamp north of Charleston, S.C.; no date (spec. A.M.N.H.).

10. Savannah River, Barnwell Co., S.C.; 1898; T. M. Ashe (A. T. Wayne, 1910).
   Savannah River, Allendale Co., S.C.; Sept. 1907; G. N. Bailie (E. E. Murphey).

11. Frequently between Augusta and Savannah along the Savannah River; about 1800; Alexander Wilson (1811).

12. Hunting Id., Beaufort Co., S.C.; before 1870; W. Hoxie (Hasbrouck).

13. Johnson's, Pritchard's, and Edding Islands, S.C.; 1880 and before; W. Hoxie (1885, and Hasbrouck).

(Habitat outlines drawn from Marbut's 'Soils of the United States.')

GEORGIA-NORTHERN FLORIDA REGION

(Fig. 4)

1. Altamaha River, Tattnall Co., Ga.; around 1925; Vester Brown (verbal).

2. Altamaha Swamp, Ga.; between 1853 and 1865; Dr. S. W. Wilson (H. B. Bailey 1883).

3. Small tributary of the Satilla River, 20 mi. se. Blackshear, Ga.; about 1895; Maurice Thompson (1896).

4. Okefenokee, Ga.; 1860; S. C. Dinwiddie (spec. U.S. Nat. Mus.)
   Craven Hammock, Okefenokee Swamp, Ga.; 1910–15; Sam Mizell (verbal).

5. Minnie Lake Island, Okefenokee Swamp, Ga.; 1910–15; Sam Mizell (verbal).

6. Okefenokee Region, Ga.; about 1888; Maurice Thompson (1889).

7. East side of the Suwannee Canal, Okefenokee Swamp, Ga.; 1910–15; Sam Mizell (verbal).

8. About a day's journey down the river from Columbus, Ga.; 1887; August Koch (1888).

9. Bristol, Fla.; Dec. 1889 (Hasbrouck).

10. Apalachicola River swamp, Fla.; March 1887; August Koch (1888).

11. Apalachicola River swamp; 1920; resident's report (A. H. Howell, 1932).
Apalachicola River swamp; about 1935; Mr. Stensal and others (verbal).

12. Wakulla Co., Fla.; June 1936 and Jan. 1937; George Van Hyning (verbal).

13. Leon Co., Fla.; about 1900; R. W. Williams (1904).

14. "Several miles upstream," St. Marks River, Fla.; Apr. 1886; H. A. Kline (1887).

15. St. Marks, Fla.; March 1885; H. A. Kline (1886).
St. Marks, Fla.; Jan. 1900; C. J. Pennock (1901).

16. Waukeenah River, Jefferson Co., Fla.; Apr. 1894 (A. T. Wayne's field catalogue, No. 3035).

17. Wacissa River region, Jefferson Co., Fla.; Feb. to June 1894; A. T. Wayne (1895) (spec. M.C.Z.).
Wacissa River; Dec. 15, 1932; C. R. Aschmeier (A. H. Howell, epist.).

18. Wacissa River swamp, Fla.; 1923; resident's report (A. H. Howell, 1932).
Wacissa River swamp; up to 1937; J. B. Royalls (verbal).

19. Aucilla River, Fla.; 1894; A. T. Wayne (field catalogue).
Aucilla River, Fla.; May 1917; C. J. Pennock (spec. Acad. Nat. Sci.).

20. Taylor Co., Fla., Big Muddy swamp; Feb. 1894; A. T. Wayne (field catalogue).

21. Taylor Co., Fla.; Jan. 1900; C. J. Pennock (1901).

22. Taylor Co., Fla.; March 1904; R. D. Hoyt (1905).

23. Stephensville, Taylor Co., Fla.; Jan. 1901; C. J. Pennock (spec. Acad. Nat. Sci.).

24. Lafayette or Dixie Co., Fla.; 1905 (spec. M.C.Z.).

25. Pumpkin swamp, Dixie Co., Fla.; Apr. 1893; A. T. Wayne (field catalogue).

26. California swamp, Dixie Co., Fla.; Feb. 1893; A. T. Wayne (field catalogue).

27. California swamp; 1893 (spec. M.C.Z.).

28. Branford, Fla.; Apr. 1892; A. T. Wayne (field catalogue).

29. Suwannee River, near Old Town, Fla.; 1890 (spec. A.M.N.H.), and 1893 (spec. M.C.Z.).

30. Old Town, Fla.; Apr. 1892; A. T. Wayne (spec. M.C.Z.).

31. Suwannee Hammock, Levy Co., Fla.; 1893; A. T. Wayne (field catalogue).

Fig. 4. Ivory-billed Woodpecker distribution, Georgia–northern Florida region.

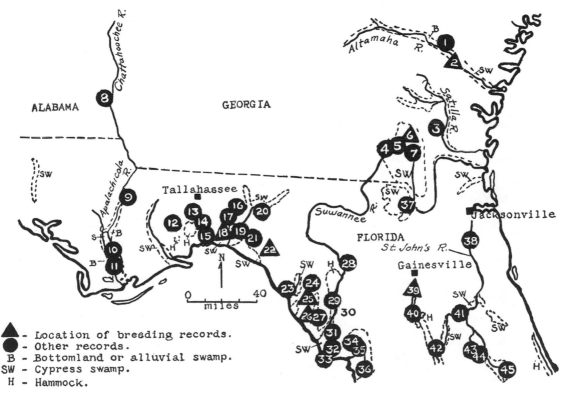

Suwannee Hammock; 1917; C. J. Pennock (epist.).
Suwannee Hammock; about 1925; Dr. Turner (verbal).

32. Rosewood, Fla.; 1881–83; C. J. Maynard (spec. M.C.Z.).
33. Cedar Keys, Fla.; Jan. 1859; G. Wurdeman (spec. U.S. Nat. Mus.).
34. Otter Creek, Gulf Hammock, Levy Co., Fla.; about 1905; Theodore Gordon (1909).
35. Gulf Hammock, Levy Co., Fla.; Aug. 1883 (spec. M.C.Z.).
    Gulf Hammock, Levy Co.; March 1887; Phillip Laurent (1887).
36. Sim's Ridge, Gulf Hammock, Levy Co., Fla.; 1932–34; T. Roy Young (epist.).
37. Baker Co., Fla.; no date (spec. col. Charles Doe).
38. St. John's River, north of Green Cove Springs, Fla.; 1887; C. T. Adams (spec. A.M.N.H.).
39. Alachua Co., Fla.; about 1910; O. E. Baynard (1913).
40. Micanopy, Fla.; 1909; O. E. Baynard (Biol. Surv. Notes).
41. St. John's and Ocklawaha Rivers, Fla.; 1873; C. H. Merriam (1874).
    Between Welaka and Rodman, Fla.; 1916; O. E. Baynard (Biol. Surv. Notes).
42. Oklawaha River swamp, Fla.; 1879 (spec. F.M.); and 1923; B. M. Kinser (A. H. Howell, 1932).
43. Juniper Creek, Marion Co., Fla.; March 1886; E. M. Hasbrouck (1891).
44. Lake George, Fla.; July 1877; T. W. Wilson (spec. U.S. Nat. Mus.).
45. Volusia, Fla.; Feb. 1869; J. A. Allen (spec. M.C.Z.).

(Habitat outlines drawn from Marbut's 'Soils of the United Sates,' for Georgia, and from Florida Agricultural Experiment Station's vegetation map of Florida.)

SOUTHERN FLORIDA REGION

(Fig. 5)

1. Mouth Withlacoochee River; 1879–80; W. E. D. Scott (1881).
2. Crystal River, Citrus Co.; July 1, 1889 (spec. M.C. Z.).
3. Panasofkee Lake, Sumter Co.; spring 1876; W. E. D. Scott (1881).
4. Wekiva River; June 7, 1878 (spec. M.C.Z.).
   Wekiva River; about 1885; G. A. Boardman (1885).
5. Enterprise (now Benson Springs), Volusia Co.; about 1859; H. Bryant (1859).
   Enterprise; Mar. 5, 1869; J. A. Allen (1871).
6. Hawkinsville; Mar. 15, 1869; J. A. Allen (1871) (spec. M.C.Z.).
   Lake Jessup; winter 1869 (spec. M.C.Z.).
   Sanford; around 1885; C. D. Barrett (anon., 1885).
7. Lake Harney; no date but old (egg col. Univ. Fla. Mus.).

8. Turnbull Swamp or Hammock, Volusia Co.; 1872; (S. C. Clarke).
   Turnbull Swamp or Hammock; 1907 and 1911; Mrs. Sams (A. W. Butler, 1931).
9. Indian River; Feb. 3, 1885 (spec. A.M.N.H.).
10. Hernando Co.; Mar. 18, 1876 and Jan. 17, 1877 (spec. M.C.Z.).
11. Linden; Mar. 30, 1886 (spec. M.C.Z.).
12. Lake Co., 15 mi. s. Clermont; Mar. 4, 1904; R. D. Hoyt (1905).
    Lake Co.; Mar. 10, 1905; R. D. Hoyt (egg col. M.C.Z.).
13. Polk Co.; 1889 (spec. M.C.Z.).
    Northwest of Polk City, Polk Co.; about 1930; O. E. Baynard (verbal).
14. Davenport; June 10, 1889 (spec. M.C.Z.).
15. Gotha, Orange Co.; 1906; J. T. Mason (spec. Colo. Mus. N.H.).
    Bear Bay, west Orange Co.; Oct. 1913 (Biol. Surv. Notes).
16. Reedy Creek, Polk Co.; about 1930; John Goodman (verbal).
    Reedy Creek; Oct. 1892; Smith (A. T. Wayne's field catalogue).
17. Kissimmee; 1887 (spec. F.M.); and about 1900; W. B. Hinton (Howe and King, 1902).
18. Jim Creek, Orange Co.; Dec. 1936; G. E. McCulloch (verbal).
19. Taylor Creek, Osceola Co.; about 1916; Nicholson and James Black (verbal).
20. Taylor Creek; 1907 (spec. F.M.); and Apr. 1924; A. A. Allen (Allen and Kellogg, 1937) (spec. Univ. Fla. Mus.).
21. Wolf Creek, Osceola Co.; D. J. Nicholson (1926).
22. Merritt's Island; 1870; S. C. Clarke (1885).
23. North Lake Washington; Dec. 1902 (spec. M.C.Z.). Brevard Co.; winter 1901 (spec. M.C.Z.).
24. Cypress swamp near Tarpon Springs; Mar. 1887; W. E. D. Scott (1888) (spec. M.C.Z.).
26. Clearwater; 1880; W. E. D. Scott (1881).
27. Tampa; Sept. 1883 (spec. M.C.Z.).
28. Tampa; 1883–89 (spec. M.C.Z. and A.M.N.H.).
29. Hillsborough Co.; no date; Scott (spec. A.M.N.H.).
30. Manatee Co.; March 17, 1889 (spec. M.C.Z.).
31. Manatee Creek, Manatee Co. (T33S, R22E, S34); no date (nest spec. Univ. Fla. Mus.).
32. Highlands Hammock, Highlands Co.; 1937; O. E. Baynard (1937).
33. Kissimmee River, 50 mi. below Kissimmee; Nov. 1908; Tom Murray (Butler, 1931).
34. Fort Drum; May 1899; Hoxie (Biol. Surv. Notes).
35. DeSoto Co.; no date (Hargitt).
36. Lake Okeechobee; 1898 (spec. F.M.); and Feb. 1904 (spec. M.C.Z.).
37. Punta Gorda; Jan. 1904; J. R. Jack (spec. A.M.N. H.).
38. Fort Myers; 1891; W. E. D. Scott (spec. M.C.Z.).
39. Caloosahatchie region; 1891; W. E. D. Scott (1892).

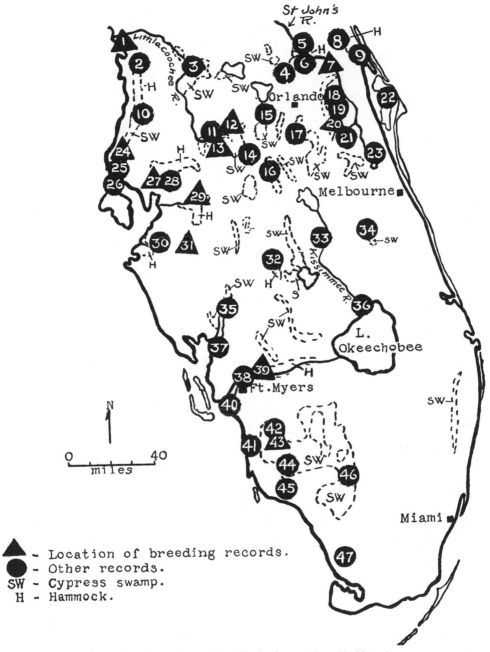

Fig. 5.   Ivory-billed Woodpecker distribution, southern Florida region.

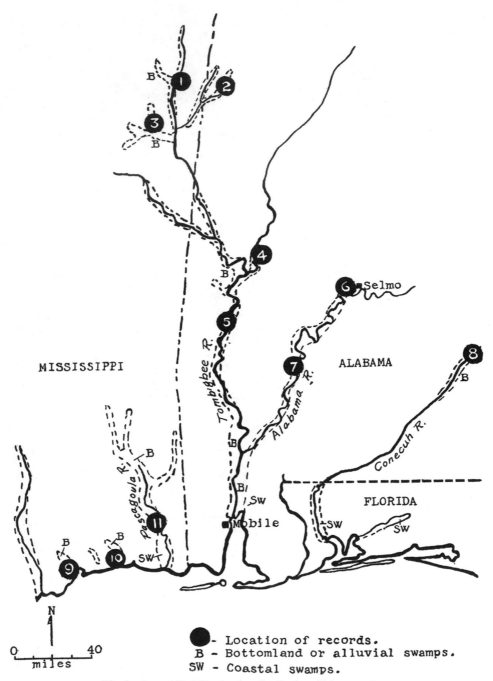

Fig. 6.   Ivory-billed Woodpecker distribution, Alabama region.

40. Punta Rassa; 1889; Mr. Atkins (Scott, 1889). Punta Rassa; Feb. 1904 (spec. M.C.Z.).
41. Naples; Apr. 1902 (spec. M.C.Z.).
42. Big Cypress, Lee Co.; March 1911; O. E. Baynard (1914, and verbal).
    Big Cypress, Lee Co.; March 1913; Phelps (1914).
43. Big Cypress; Feb. 15, 1898; Robert Ridgway (1898, and spec. U.S. Nat. Mus.).
44. Big Cypress near Deep Lake; Feb. 1914; F. H. Kennard (1915, and spec. M.C.Z.).
45. Near Everglades; 1917; J. B. Ellis (1918).
46. Big Cypress, East Crossing region; around 1937; James Thorpe and others (verbal).
47. Shark River and Lostman's River; around 1935; J. M. Roberts and others (verbal).

(Habitat outlines drawn from Florida Agricultural Experiment Station's vegetation map of Florida.)

The following places in Florida were not located:
Argo; no date (Hargitt).
Blackwater River; no date (spec. F.M.).
Fort Capron near Kissimmee River; about 1916; Dr. Ernest I. Shores (W. F. Henninger).
Lentes Landing; about 1878; T. W. Wilson (anon., 1879).
Wa-hoo or Warwhoop Hammock; 1889; R. B. Whitehead (1892).

ALABAMA REGION

(Fig. 6)

1. Monroe Co., Miss.; 1885; G. V. Young (Hasbrouck).
2. Crump Springs, Buttahatchie River; 1886; G. V. Young (Hasbrouck).
3. Clay Co., Miss.; 1885; G. V. Young (Hasbrouck).
4. Cypress Slough, 10 mi. w. Greensboro, Hale Co., Ala.; 1886; W. C. Avery (1890).
5. Tombigbee River, Marengo Co., Miss.; 1865; W. C. Avery (Hasbrouck).
6. Near the Alabama River and Selma, Ala.; around 1850; P. H. Gosse (1859).
7. Wilcox Co., Ala.; 1889; G. V. Young (Hasbrouck).
8. Conecuh swamps, n. of Troy, Ala.; 1907; C. W. Howe (A. H. Howell, 1907).
9. Near Bay St. Louis, Miss.; Jan. 1885; M. Thompson (1889).
10. Mississippi City, Miss.; March 29, 1893 (spec. A.M.N.H.).
11. Pascagoula swamp, Jackson Co., Miss.; Dec. 1921; J. D. Corrington (1922).

(Habitat outlines drawn from Marbut's 'Soils of the United States.')

LOWER MISSISSIPPI DELTA

(Fig. 7)

1. Sunflower Delta, Miss.; about 1888; Coahoma (1888).

2. Yazoo River Delta, Miss.; 1890; B. Young (Hasbrouck).
3. Prairie Mer Rouge, La.; 1853; J. Fairie (H. C. Oberholser, 1938).
4. Bowling Green, West Carroll Parish, La.; Aug. 1903; E. L. Moseley (C. Cottam and P. Knappen).
   Boeuf River swamp, West Carroll Parish, La.; about 1912; E. L. Moseley (1928) and J. Ward (verbal).
5. Bayou Macon swamp, West Carroll Parish, La.; 1926; E. L. Moseley (1928).
6. Tensas River swamp, East Carroll Parish, La.; about 1930; Ben Barmore (verbal).
7. Bear Lake, Madison Parish, La.; Feb. 1904; Ned Hollister (H. C. Oberholser, 1938).
   Near Bear Lake, Madison Parish; Sept. 1937; J. J. Kuhn (verbal).
8. Madison Parish, La.; March 1891; E. M. Haskell (spec. A.M.N.H.); and 1909 (spec. A.M.N.H.).
9. Tensas River swamp, Madison Parish, La.; Apr. 1932; T. G. Pearson (1932).
   Tensas River swamp, Madison Parish, La.; Apr.–May 1935; Allen and Kellogg (1937).
   Tensas River swamp, Madison Parish, La.; 1937–39; many observations; Tanner.
10. Roaring Bayou, Franklin Parish, La.; July 1899; G. E. Beyer (1900).
11. Tensas Parish, n. of St. Joseph, La.; May 1929; Earl R. Smith (epist.).
12. Tensas and Concordia Parishes, La.; R. H. Stirling (Biol. Surv. Notes).
13. Bayou Sara, W. Feliciana Parish, La.; June 1821; J. Audubon (H. C. Oberholser, 1938).
14. Bayou des Ourses, St. Martin Parish, La.; about 1920; Charles Frederick (verbal).
15. Cow Bayou, Iberville Parish, La.; Mar. 1906; B. V. Lilly (spec. col. U.S. Fish & Wildlife Service).
16. Catahoula Lake, St. Martin Parish, La.; about 1920 (verbal).
17. Avery Island, Iberia Parish, La.; 1892; E. A. McIlhenny (Bendire); 1895 (spec. Cornell Univ.).
    Avery Island; 1900–23; E. A. McIlhenny (1941).
18. Lafourche Parish, La.; 1918 (S. C. Arthur, 1918).

(Habitat outlines drawn from Putnam and Bull's 'Trees of the Bottomlands of the Mississippi River Delta'; Winters, Putnam, and Eldredge's 'Forest Resources of the North Louisiana Delta'; and Marbut's 'Soils of the United States.')

UPPER MISSISSIPPI DELTA

(Fig. 8)

1. White Co., 40 mi. south Mount Carmel, Ill.; about 1852; Robert Ridgway (1889 and 1915).
2. Junction of Ohio and Mississippi Rivers; about 1825; J. J. Audubon (1831).
3. Little River, Stoddard Co., Mo.; Nov. 1895 (Otto Widman, 1907).

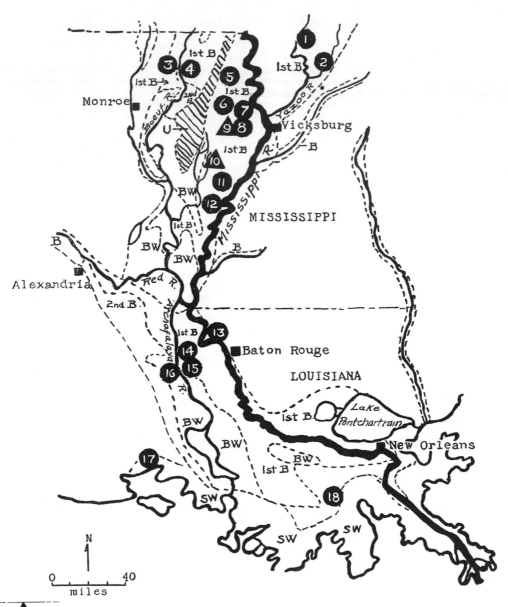

Fig. 7. Ivory-billed Woodpecker distribution, lower Mississippi delta region.

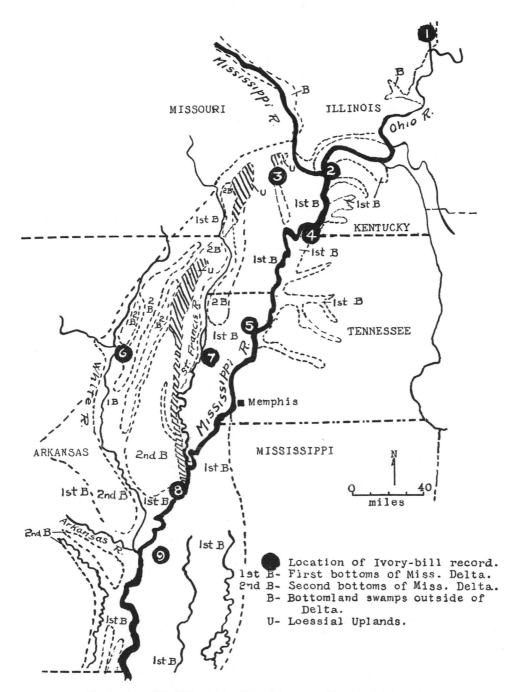

Fig. 8. Ivory-billed Woodpecker distribution, upper Mississippi delta region.

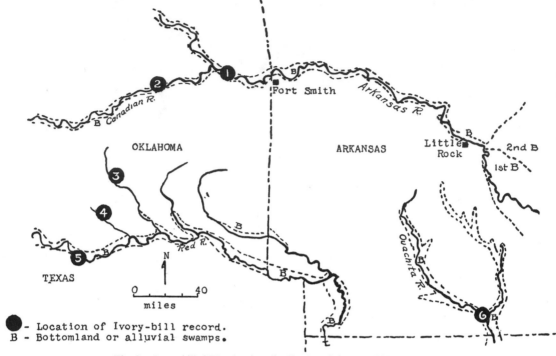

Fig. 9.   Ivory-billed Woodpecker distribution, Arkansas–Oklahoma region.

4. Fulton Co., Ky.; 1872–74 (L. O..Pindar, 1925).
5. Osceola, Mississippi Co., Ark.; 1887; Dr. Richardson (A. H. Howell, 1911).
    Northeastern Arkansas; 1888 (W. W. Cooke, 1888).
6. Newport, Jackson Co., Ark.; about 1885; Yell (1885).
7. Marked Tree, Poinsett Co., Ark.; March 1889; L. O. Pindar (1924).
8. Helena, Phillips Co., Ark.; 1912; Stephenson (Biol. Surv. Notes).
9. Bolivar Co., Miss.; March 1893 (spec. Acad. Nat. Sci.).

(Habitat outlines drawn from Putnam and Bull's 'Trees of the Bottomlands of the Mississippi Delta Region,' and from Marbut's 'Soils of the United States.')

ARKANSAS–OKLAHOMA REGION

(Fig. 9)

1. Timber of the Arkansas River; 1850; S. W. Woodhouse (1853).
2. Near the 'falls' of the Canadian River, Ark.; 1820; Edwin James (1905).
3. Old Boggy Depot, Atoka Co., Okla.; 1870–74; Miss M. H. Wright (M. M. Nice, 1931).

4. Blue River, near Caddo, Okla.; 1883–84; W. W. Cooke (1914).
5. Cooke Co., Tex.; about 1875; G. H. Ragsdale (Hasbrouck).
6. Ouachita River, near junction of Caddo River; 1834; G. W. Featherstonhaugh (1835).

EAST TEXAS REGION

(Fig. 10)

1. Neches River, Jasper Co., Texas; May 3, 1885; B. F. Goss (Hasbrouck, Bendire).
3. Tarkington, Texas; Nov. 26, 1904; V. Bailey; (2 spec. U.S. Fish & Wildlife Service).
4. Trinity River, Texas; 1864; H. E. Dresser (1865).
5. Northern Harris Co., Texas; about 1880; H. Nehrling (1882).
6. Buffalo Bayou, Texas; around 1840; Audubon (1842).
7. Brazos River, Texas; around 1880; R. M. Conway (J. M. H.).
8. Brazos River, Texas; May 1864; H. E. Dresser (1865).

(Habitat outlines for the last two regions listed drawn from Marbut's 'Soils of the United States.')

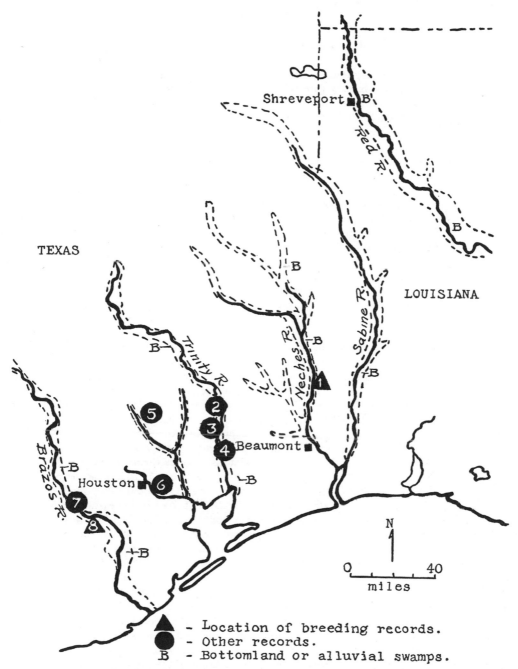

Fig. 10.   Ivory-billed Woodpecker distribution, east Texas region.

CHAPTER 3

Habitats of the Ivory-billed Woodpecker

O N THE regional maps showing the distribution of the Ivory-billed Woodpecker (preceding chapter), the spots marking the location of Ivory-bill records were placed as accurately as possible to enable correlation of the locations with swamp and other types of habitat. Accurate placing was not possible for some records because of the indefiniteness of the data, especially where the names of towns or counties alone were given as the locality. This would introduce some untrue variation, but the maps show plainly that all Ivory-bill records have been located in or very near swamps or Florida hammocks. Outside of the Florida region, alluvial swamps and river bottoms were the habitat of the Ivory-bill; in and near Florida the Ivory-bill also inhabited cypress swamps away from rivers and swampy hammocks.

Material for the descriptions of these habitats was gathered during the field work, when many virgin and primitive tracts of forest and swamp were visited. Records and descriptions of the composition of the different types of forests were made at those times.

For purposes of description, habitats of the Ivory-bill range have been classified as follows: river bottoms (outside of the Mississippi Delta), bottomlands of the Mississippi Delta, and Florida region.

River Bottoms (outside of the Mississippi Delta)

The larger rivers of the southern states that drain the piedmont or hilly sections and flow either into the Atlantic or Gulf of Mexico all have alluvial bottomland along their courses. The largest area of bottomland belongs to the Mississippi Delta, and because of its size that area is treated separately.

A general description of these river bottoms will apply to all those to be discussed. The rivers drain clay hill country, and the soil of their bottoms is an alluvial clay that is usually flooded annually. Along the upper courses of these rivers the bottoms are comparatively high and dry, the soil less water-soaked and usually flooded a short portion of the year. These parts of the bottomland are timbered with oak, sweet gum, ash, and other hardwoods. Downriver the bottoms become more of a real swamp where the soil is covered with water much of the year, and the timber is mainly cypress and tupelo gum. The lower twenty to thirty miles of these rivers are mostly of this type. Loblolly and long-leaf pine woods border all these river swamps.

In the localities where Ivory-bills have been observed, both the oak-sweet gum and the cypress-tupelo forests are present, but the oak-sweet gum usually predominates.

In the Carolina and Georgia regions, most of the Ivory-bill records are along the Pee Dee, Santee, Savannah, and Altamaha Rivers; all of these rivers drain the piedmont section. Dominant forest species on the drier sites of these bottoms (Plate 2) are sweet gum, laurel oak, and water oak. Associated with the predominants are overcup oak, cow oak, water hickory, green ash, and white elm. Smaller trees, usually not in the dominant crown, are red maple, American holly and ironwood, and there are also present a few other trees of species not mentioned.

The cypress-tupelo association, present in the wet swamps of these southeastern river bottoms (Plate 3), has as dominant species bald cypress and tupelo gum. Associated with them are red maple, overcup oak, and cottonwood.

In the Gulf coast region east of the Mississippi, Ivory-bills have been observed along most of the larger rivers. The composition of the forests along these rivers differs very little from that described for the Carolina and Georgia regions.

West of the Mississippi Delta, in the east Texas region, the sweet gum-oak association consists of sweet gum and willow oak as the dominant species, with overcup oak, water hickory, green ash, black gum, and cedar elm as important associates. The cypress-tupelo association is present in the wetter parts of the swamp and differs very little from that described for the Carolina and Georgia regions.

14

Bottomlands of the Mississippi Delta

The Mississippi Delta, the alluvial bottom of the Mississippi River, stretches from the junction of the Ohio and Mississippi Rivers to the Gulf of Mexico, and is from forty to eighty miles wide. Most of the Delta lies on the west of the river, the Yazoo basin in Mississippi being the only large part of it east of the river. The important difference between the Delta and bottomlands of other rivers is its large size, with a consequent greater variety of forest sites which are often of considerable area. Certain forest types, which may not be recognizable in smaller river bottoms because of the limited area they occupy, cover hundreds of square miles in the Delta.

Almost all of the Ivory-bill records in the Mississippi Delta occur in the first bottoms outside of the backwater and swamp areas, as can be seen from the two maps covering the region. The Ivory-bill's distribution in the Delta was apparently limited to the higher parts of these first bottoms.

These higher areas are rarely covered with water more than a very few months of the year; the soil is a moderately well-drained alluvial clay. The forest is a sweet gum-oak association (Plate 4), and the dominant tree species are sweet gum, bottomland red or Nuttall's oak, and green ash. Associated with these are willow oak, water oak, overcup oak, American or white elm, cedar elm, hackberry, water hickory, and pecan. Lesser trees present in some numbers are red maple, honey locust, and persimmon.

The lower parts of the first bottoms are in backwater areas or in true swamps. The backwater areas, where the soil is very poorly drained but not covered with water most of the year, are forested with an overcup oak-water hickory association, which is two-thirds overcup oak and water hickory, with a few associates of bottomland red oak, water locust, green ash, persimmon, and cedar elm. Swamp areas, where the ground is covered with water most of the year, are timbered with cypress-tupelo forest, the same as described for other bottomlands.

The second bottoms of the Mississippi Delta, which are better drained than the first, are mostly timbered with an oak-hickory association. The dominant trees are white oak, delta post oak, cherrybark oak, cow oak, willow oak, water oak, and bitternut and other hickories.

The distribution of the Ivory-bill in the Mississippi Delta has been almost confined to the higher parts of the first bottoms where the forest of sweet gum, bottomland red oak, ash, and elm predominates. During my field work in the Singer Tract, in the heart of the first bottoms, I found that the Ivory-bills there lived almost entirely in the parts of the forest where the sweet gum-oak association predominated, and rarely entered the flats where those trees were lacking and the overcup oak-water hickory association stood. Correlated with this, or more likely a cause of this, is the fact that in the Singer Tract the Ivory-bills fed upon sweet gum trees more than any other tree, with bottomland red oak next in preference. The feeding habits of the bird will be discussed more thoroughly later.

Florida Region

The Florida region is far from uniform, even in the nature of its swampland. In all, or almost all, of the Ivory-bill localities in the Florida region, cypress is one, if not the one, dominant tree; this is the basis for the common belief that the Ivory-bill's habitat is everywhere in heavy cypress swamps. But except for this predominance of cypress, there is little other uniformity over the Florida region.

The dominance of cypress in the bird's habitat is a condition not found outside of the Florida region. Another difference is that Ivory-bills in Florida frequently fed in the pine woods bordering the swamps, something that has never been recorded in the region of the Mississippi Delta and only rarely elsewhere.

In northern Florida, Ivory-bills occurred mostly along the Apalachicola River, which has a typical river-bottom swamp, and in the river swamps from the St. Marks to the Suwannee. The swamps along the Suwannee, Wacissa, and neighboring rivers (Plate 5) are not bottomland swamps but are forested with a cypress-black gum association: bald cypress, black gum, and green ash as predominants, associated with red maple, red bay, sweet bay, laurel oak, American elm, and cabbage palmetto. A. T. Wayne (1893), writing of the Suwannee River region, described the Ivory-bill as nesting in the swamps of that region and feeding in the burned-over parts of the woods where there were fire-killed trees.

The Okefenokee Swamp perhaps should not be included in the Florida region since it is mostly within the state of Georgia, but it resembles the Florida region more than any other. Sam Mizell reported (verbally) that he used to see Ivory-bills in the Okefenokee in red bay-cypress swamps or bays, frequently near pine islands. The trees in these 'tan bays' are almost entirely of red bay and pond cypress; the surrounding deep swamp is a practically pure stand of pond cypress. Accounts of Ivory-bills in the Okefenokee region are too few and vague to be of any value in understanding the region from the standpoint of the birds.

In the central part of Florida are many marl hammocks, growths of hardwood trees usually mixed with some swamp, from which Ivory-bill records have come. The Gulf Hammock in Levy County is the largest; the one along the Caloosa-hatchie River is the most southerly large hammock outside of the tropical zone in Florida. The forest growth in these hammocks varies greatly, almost from pineland to swamps, depending on the site. Trees in the drier parts of the Gulf Hammock, in the northern part of central Florida, are the loblolly pine, red cedar, live oak, laurel oak, cow oak, magnolia, red bay, other hardwoods, and cabbage palmetto; in sloughs in the hammock are bald cypress and black gum. Hammocks in south-central Florida have the typical slash pine, laurel oak, live oak, red bay, sweet bay, red maple, and cabbage palmetto.

The swamps of central and southern Florida (Plate 6) have many Ivory-bill records. Most of these swamps are along creeks and small rivers and are timbered mainly with bald cypress, such as the creek swamps in eastern Orange County. Predominant trees there are bald cypress, red maple, laurel oak, black and some sweet gum and cabbage palmetto. In this area Arthur A. Allen (Allen and Kellogg) found Ivory-bills nesting in the swamps and going into the pinelands to feed on fire-killed trees. Florida has many cypress heads or ponds, wet depressions which are wooded

with pond cypress, but these are rarely visited by Ivory-bills. The Big Cypress Swamp, mostly in Collier County, is the largest area of cypress swamp in the state and, being in the tropical zone, it has many species of trees not found in other swamps. Bald cypress is still dominant and forms an almost pure stand in some places. Associated with the cypress in varying numbers are red maple, pop ash, pond apple, laurel oak, wild fig, cabbage palmetto, and locally, royal palm. The few times that Ivory-bills have been observed in the Big Cypress, they have been in parts of the swamp where cypress was abundant.

Summary of the Ivory-billed Woodpecker's Habitat

There is no one type of forest that is the habitat of the Ivory-billed Woodpecker; it varies greatly in different sections of the bird's range. In some parts of its range, however, the Ivory-bill's distribution is closely correlated with certain types of forest. In the Mississippi Delta the bird was practically confined to the higher parts of the first bottoms where sweet gum, bottomland red oak, and green ash predominated, and in that area they fed mostly upon sweet gum and bottomland red oak. In bottomland forests outside of the Mississippi Delta, Ivory-bills likewise preferred woods that predominated in sweet gum and oaks, although in this area laurel oak and water oak were the common oaks. The birds also appeared in other types of forest, such as cypress-tupelo swamps, perhaps because they had more variety of forest in their range due to the smaller size of the river bottoms.

In the swamps and hammocks of Florida the Ivory-bill was not confined to any particular type of forest, nor was there any one characteristic of the woods throughout the bird's habitat there that appeared to have an important influence on its distribution. Cypress is present in all the swamps in Florida; Ivory-bills frequently nested in cypress trees but only occasionally fed upon them. In Florida these woodpeckers fed more among the pine woods than they did in other regions. In the hammocks that they frequently occupied, hardwood trees were by far the most abundant. This apparent toleration of habitat shown by the Ivory-bill in Florida is perhaps the

Plate 1.   Male Ivory-bill returning to relieve female.   April 1935.

Plate 2.   Sweet gum and oak bottomland forest of the Carolina region, Black Oak Island, S. C.

Plate 3.   Cypress and tupelo gum swamp, Wadmacaun Island, S. C.

Plate 4.   Sweet gum and oak forest of the Mississippi Delta, Madison Parish, La.

Plate 5. Swamp forest in northern Florida, Suwannee River swamp.

Plate 6. Swamp forest in southern Florida, Big Cypress.

reason why the Ivory-bill was more common and more widely distributed there than in any other state.

One condition is characteristic of all Ivory-bill habitats, namely, that other species of wood-peckers are common or abundant in those places. Species like the Pileated and Red-bellied Wood-peckers, having a comparatively widespread and general distribution and inhabiting a variety of woods, reach their greatest abundance in the kinds of forests inhabited by Ivory-bills. Those forests, whether they are in river bottoms or swamps and hammocks in Florida, possess the optimum conditions for woodpeckers.

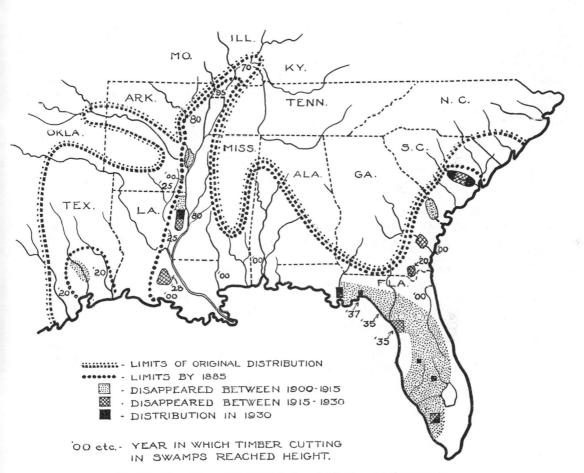

▦▦▦▦▦	- LIMITS OF ORIGINAL DISTRIBUTION
●●●●●●	- LIMITS BY 1885
▦	- DISAPPEARED BETWEEN 1900-1915
▨	- DISAPPEARED BETWEEN 1915-1930
■	- DISTRIBUTION IN 1930

'OO etc.- YEAR IN WHICH TIMBER CUTTING
          IN SWAMPS REACHED HEIGHT.

Fig. 11.   Map of Ivory-billed Woodpecker distribution and disappearance.

CHAPTER 4

History of the Disappearance of the Ivory-billed Woodpecker

THE numbers and distribution of the Ivory-billed Woodpecker began to shrink noticeably in the latter half of the nineteenth century. By 1885 the birds had disappeared from North Carolina and northern South Carolina and from all the region west of the Mississippi Delta excepting the very southeastern part of Texas. By 1900 they were gone from almost all of Alabama and Mississippi. By 1915 they had disappeared from Texas, Arkansas, and Alabama, and from most of Florida, Georgia, and South Carolina, and there they remained only in the larger swamps. These ranges dwindled or disappeared until by 1930 Ivory-bills were known only from the Santee swamp in South Carolina, a few scattered localities in Florida, and northeastern Louisiana.

The restriction of the Ivory-bill's range is shown on the map (Fig. 11). Examining the map, it appears that the period of greatest range restriction outside of Florida occurred between 1885 and 1900; in Florida the greatest restriction of the bird's range occurred between 1900 and 1915.

It had long been recognized that the Ivory-bill was usually confined to the virgin forests and had retreated or disappeared at the felling of these forests. An attempt was therefore made to see if there was any correlation between the restriction of the Ivory-bill's distribution and the advance of logging over the country. The history of logging in this country is an almost unexplored field, and I found no really good source for ascertaining the date when areas, especially swamp areas, of the southeastern states were logged over. For most states, the only source was the United States census reports, which give the number of men employed and the total cost of raw materials in the lumber industry, and so is a rough index of the rate of logging within a state. Dr. R. K. Winters, of the Southern Forest Experiment Station, kindly gave me what information he had on the dates of logging activity in the Mississippi Delta; Mr. Williams of the Kirby Lumber Corp.,

Houston, did the same for eastern Texas, and Sam Mizell, Okefenokee Wildlife Refuge, for the Okefenokee swamp of Georgia. From these sources I have tried to find out when the different regions were logged and when most or all of the virgin timber was removed.

Dates for the disappearance of the Ivory-bill from a region and for the logging of the region can best be presented and compared in the form of the following table.

COMPARISON OF TIME OF IVORY-BILL DISAPPEARANCE WITH TIME OF LOGGING

Locality or region	Period during which Ivory-bills disappeared	Remarks on state of logging industry
Missouri	1885–1900	Logging active in 1890
Most of Arkansas	1885–1900	Logging increased rapidly between 1890 and 1900
Most of Mississippi	1885–1900	The number of men doubled and the total cost of raw materials tripled in the lumber industry between 1890 and 1900
Most of Alabama	1885–1900	Lumber industry tripled in size between 1880 and 1890; Mobile Delta almost completely cut by 1900
Most of Florida	1900–1915	Lumber industry showed biggest increase between 1900 and 1910
Eastern Texas	Last Ivory-bill record in 1904	Logging of swamp hardwoods finished soon after 1915
Southern Lousiana Delta	Last Ivory-bill record in 1920	Cutting of swamp timber started around 1905 and finished in 1928
Northern Louisiana Delta	Last Ivory-bill record outside of Singer Tract in 1929	Logging of swamp timber reached its peak in this region in 1925

18

In the states of Missouri, Arkansas, Mississippi, Alabama, and Florida, the time of the Ivory-bill's disappearance from all or most of its former range coincided at least roughly with a time of active or rapidly increasing logging. Considering the meager information at hand that is about all that can be said for those regions. The last Ivory-bill record for eastern Texas is eleven years ahead of the time of active logging, 1915, in the swamps of that region, but of course Ivory-bills might have lived there unobserved long after 1904.

The logging history of the lower Mississippi Delta swamps is better known than for most other large regions, and shows a closer correlation between the times of logging and the disappearance of the Ivory-bill. Logging started in the southern part of Louisiana around 1905 and gradually spread northward. The southern half, below the Red River, was almost completely cut over by 1928; the last Ivory-bill reports for this region were for 1920. Logging began to extend from Arkansas southward into Louisiana about 1910. These two movements of logging, one from the south and one from the north, met in northern Louisiana, where logging reached its peak about 1925 and then declined with the exhaustion of the forests. It is there that the last remnant of virgin timber, in the Singer Tract, and the last Ivory-billed Woodpeckers of that region survive.

South Carolina and Georgia are two regions about which little can be said, for lack of information. In both of these states the cutting of swamp timber followed considerably after the peak of the pine industry, which came later in South Carolina. In South Carolina, also, large tracts of virgin swamp timber persisted longer and the Ivory-bill survived longer.

The history of small areas often shows a clearer picture of the Ivory-bill's disappearing with the cutting of the forests. The last record for an Ivory-bill in the Savannah River bottoms, in 1907, was made by a man engaged in logging there (Murphey). Logging of large scale was finished in the Okefenokee swamp about 1920, and the last reliable record there was about 1912 (Sam Mizell, verbal). The last Ivory-bill reliably reported from the Gulf Hammock, Florida, was seen in 1934 (T. R. Young, epist.) in one of the very last parts of the hammock to be cut. Logging began in the Wacissa Swamps, Florida, in 1936, and was finished in 1939; the last year that the birds were seen there was in 1937 (J. B. Royalls, verbal).

E. A. McIlhenny writes (1941) that since his childhood from three to seven pairs of Ivory-bills nested yearly in the hardwood timber to the east of Avery Island, Louisiana. In 1900 cutting of this timber began along the lower Atchafalaya River to the east, and gradually worked westward. On Avery Island cutting began in 1918 and was soon completed. In 1920 "a careful search located only three of these birds. . . a single bird was seen in 1923, none since."

The story is much the same in all regions. Ivory-billed Woodpeckers have disappeared when the woods that they inhabited were cut over and the virgin timber removed. In many cases the disappearance of the birds almost coincided with the logging operations. In others there is no close correlation, but there are no records of Ivory-bills inhabiting areas for any length of time after those have been cut over.

There is one instance of Ivory-bills apparently disappearing from an area for reasons other than logging, and that is when the Ivory-bills were wiped out of the Suwannee River region of Florida by the collecting of A. T. Wayne in 1892 and 1893. Most of the seventeen Ivory-bill specimens that he secured were killed by local hunters who received a price from him. After Wayne's work there have been no reliable records of Ivory-bills being seen in that region.

CHAPTER 5

Present Distribution and Numbers of the Ivory-billed Woodpecker

FINDING the present distribution and numbers of Ivory-bills in this country was one of the first objectives of the investigation and one that consumed much time. Hunting for localities where Ivory-bills were, and in those localities trying to find the birds, was like searching for an animated needle in a haystack.

Methods Used in Hunting for Ivory-bills

At the start of the investigation two Ivory-bill localities were known, the Singer Tract in Louisiana and the Santee swamps of South Carolina. The presence of Ivory-bills in the Singer Tract had been known for some time. I saw my first one there in 1935 when accompanying an expedition from Cornell University led by Professor A. A. Allen and staffed by P. P. Kellogg, G. M. Sutton, and myself, to make sound records and motion pictures of rare birds. In the Santee region the birds had been seen by several observers, most frequently by Alexander Sprunt, Jr., but very little was known about their numbers and distribution there. Besides these two records, there were several rumors of their being in other localities. Searching for possible new Ivory-bill localities and hunting for the birds in these areas consumed about eight of the twenty-one months spent in the field.

In investigating new regions, a search was first made for suitable Ivory-bill habitat and then for any reports of the birds being in that region. Any large tract of virgin or near-virgin lowland, hardwood timber was considered a possible habitat. The most fruitful sources for locating such tracts of timber were large saw mills. The logging superintendents or woods men of these mills usually had an excellent knowledge of the region and the stands of timber, and I almost invariably met with courteous treatment and assistance when seeking information from them. I made known to them that I was working on a wildlife survey and was particularly interested in locating areas that had not been logged over. Many of these men were interested in game birds and animals, although knowledge and interest in woodpeckers was beyond them. More useful information concerning possible Ivory-bill habitats came from logging men than from any other source, and their assistance saved me a great amount of time.

Information about stands of timber was also obtained from conservation and forestry employees of both state and federal agencies, game wardens, and local people such as farmers and hunters, although reports from such local people were frequently unreliable.

Good maps assisted greatly in investigating any region, to get an understanding of the geography and the best way to get around the region. For the Mississippi Delta excellent maps were obtained from the Mississippi River Commission. The county maps of Florida published by the Florida Growers' Publishing Company, Tampa, were the best maps that I could locate for that state, although no maps were available for several counties. Soil survey maps covered a few areas I was interested in, but were hard to secure. Outside of these, good maps were almost non-existent.

An airplane was used twice in flying over new areas to 'size it up,' once over the Wacissa River and once over the Apalachicola. Properly used and with a little skill and experience, surveying from a plane is a very rapid way to get an understanding of the lay of the land, the location of the best areas, and to eliminate the completely unsuited ones.

If there seemed to be any suitable habitat for Ivory-bills in a region, a search was next made for reports of them among people who might know or have seen the birds. Local hunters, trappers, fishermen, game wardens, or any natives whose work took them into the woods were questioned. With a few exceptions amateur ornithologists were of little help because few of them were familiar with the wilder parts of the country. Game wardens frequently proved to be of most assistance, since it was within their province to be acquainted with the country and the animals in it.

It took a little experience to find the best way for questioning local people to get the desired information. The procedure that worked well was to ask them first general questions about game, wildlife, and the country, to get a general idea of what was in the region, and to judge how good and reliable observers they were. Then I asked if there were many Pileated Woodpeckers in the region, only using the local name of that bird, Lord God, Woodcock, Old Kate, or whatever it happened to be, and next whether or not there were two kinds of big woodpeckers in the country. If the answer was "yes" I tried to find how they told the two apart, and if any of the marks or calls they described resembled the Ivory-bill's. Usually the two kinds of woodpeckers they described were the Pileated and the Red-bellied, or fancied differences in the Pileated. Once in a great while I would find someone who appeared to have seen an Ivory-bill, and from him I would gather all the information I could as to when and where he saw the bird. The procedure, of course, varied greatly depending on the circumstances and the persons interviewed.

Asking local people if they knew anything about 'Ivory-billed Woodpeckers' usually elicited a blank stare, or, "Sure, they're in all the woods around here." The name meant nothing to them or they applied it to some other woodpecker. And many people gave the answer that they thought was desired, or would lead to their getting a job as guide. Consequently, letting them talk was much more successful than asking leading questions.

A picture comparing the Pileated and the Ivory-billed Woodpeckers proved very useful in such conversations. The one used was a drawing by William Montagna; the picture was reduced to $2\frac{1}{2}$ by 4 inches so that it could be easily carried in the pocket. Many copies were made and distributed among people who might help in getting information about the birds.

The practice of securing information about Ivory-bills from local people, as has been described, required the critical examination of all their remarks, and only rarely could definite conclusions be drawn from such talk. But the practice was of value, if not necessary, in getting leads and clues. Coupled with what was learned about

the possible habitats for Ivory-bills in the region, the reports of natives gave a good indication of whether or not a certain area was worth further investigation.

If there seemed to be any possibility of Ivory-bills being in an area, a hunt in the woods was made. In entering new country, I frequently employed a guide. Good guides were exceptional, and the best service that most of them could perform was understanding from my descriptions the type of forest I wanted to investigate and then leading me to the best territory. The means of getting into the woods varied greatly—foot, horseback, or boat, depending on which was most convenient.

Winter and early spring are the only good seasons for investigating Ivory-bill habitats. Leaves are then off the trees, allowing good visibility and hearing, the birds are quite active and noisy, and the cooler weather makes work in the woods pleasant. Work in the summer is practically a waste of time because of the dense vegetation, silent birds, and depressing heat.

Examining a new area, I first tried to cover it widely rather than thoroughly, to judge the suitability of the woods for Ivory-bills and to locate the most promising parts. The best areas I considered to be the ones most resembling places that Ivory-bills did inhabit, such as the Singer Tract where big sweet gums and oaks are abundant, where there are many dead and dying trees, and where other woodpeckers are common.

The most suitable areas were then examined for Ivory-bill sign, the sign that they make when feeding, and Ivory-bill holes. Ivory-bills do most of their feeding on recently dead trees, knocking off the bark to uncover and eat the borers that live between the bark and the sapwood. Ivory-bill sign shows as bare places on recently dead limbs and trees, where the bark has been scaled off clean for a considerable extent (Plates 7 and 8). Pileateds do some scaling, too, but it is usually confined to smaller limbs and to those longer dead. Freshness of the sign can be judged by any appearance of weathering, which will soon turn bare wood a grayish color. Extensive scaling of the bark from a tree which has died so recently that the bark is still tight, with a brownish or reddish color to the exposed wood showing that the work is fresh, is one good indication of the presence of Ivory-bills.

The holes that Ivory-bills dig for nesting and roosting have an oval or irregular entrance measuring about five inches vertically and four inches across, averaging about an inch larger than the Pileated's entrance hole. In the Singer Tract there were usually many scaled limbs in the neighborhood of these holes; the combination of holes and feeding sign, both resembling the work of Ivory-bills, is the most promising indication of the presence of the birds.

By far the majority of areas examined had neither enough suitable habitat nor any kind of Ivory-bill sign, so hunting was not continued in them. But where the presence of the birds was suspected, search for them began in earnest. Early morning is the best time of day to look for Ivory-bills as the birds are more active then, moving more and calling frequently. The most effective way to hunt at that time of day is to move rapidly for about a quarter mile, stop and listen for a minute or more, and move on again, going through the most likely localities and trying to cover much ground while the birds are calling. Later in the day Ivory-bills are likely to become quiet, and the woods must then be worked more thoroughly, as a man would probably have to come close to the birds, perhaps close enough to disturb them, before he would be likely to hear them. Hunting back and forth through the woods in parallel lines is sometimes possible but usually not so; taking advantage of the lay of the land and working the most promising country and the areas with the most Ivory-bill sign will cover the ground where there is the best chance of finding the birds.

All the Ivory-bills that I have ever seen I located first by hearing them call and then going to them. Under good conditions—no wind and few leaves on the trees—the loud call of an Ivory-bill can be heard for almost a quarter of a mile. Sometimes the best way to hunt is to sit still in a good locality and listen for many minutes at a time. I tried to devise some imitation of their call that would make an Ivory-bill answer, but nothing was successful. The only trick that did

work, and that not very often, was to pound loudly on a resounding stub. The Ivory-bill frequently makes a double rap, sounding like a sharp blow and its immediate echo, on hard stubs and limbs; they do it most often when disturbed. Imitating this double rap, with a club on some hard dead wood, will sometimes make the bird answer by calling or rapping itself.

In the Singer Tract where I became familiar with the territories of the Ivory-bills and knew where to look for them, it was much easier finding the birds, but even then the only way that I was fairly sure of finding them was to wait at their roosting holes either early in the morning or late in the afternoon. The birds usually roosted in the same area every night and often in the same hole, and waiting for them to come off the roost in the morning was the best way to find them. Once they had come out of their holes and started off to feed, the task was to keep up with them. They usually traveled in pairs or larger family groups. When they started off on a flight, I would wait a moment, listening to see if they had stopped within earshot. Then I would start after them, usually running as best I could until I believed I was near the birds, when I would stop and listen for a moment. If I heard nothing, I went farther in the same direction, for they usually traveled in a straight line. When I decided that I had missed them somehow, it was time to circle in one direction or another in the hope of finding them again.

Working in the Singer Tract I had the assistance of local woodsmen. J. J. Kuhn, of Tallulah, Louisiana, worked with me in 1937 and 1938, and Jesse Laird, also of Tallulah, assisted me in 1939. Both of these men were good woodsmen, Mr. Kuhn one of the best, and assisted materially. Two men working together in the same region can cover the woods more than twice as thoroughly as one man working alone; it is best to have each take half of the area that is to be covered and work at least a half mile apart.

Summary of Areas Investigated

The areas that were investigated during the Ivory-bill study for the presence and numbers of Ivory-bills are mapped on the chart (Fig. 12) and

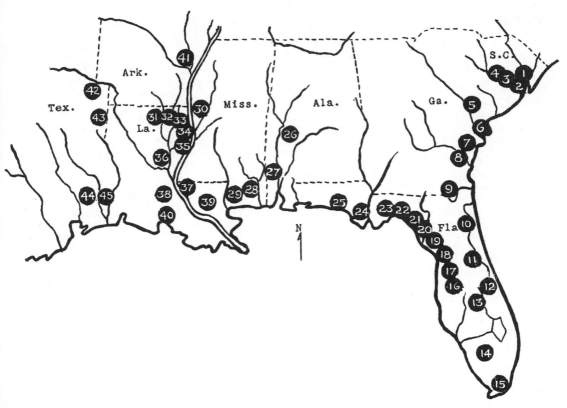

Fig. 12. Map of southeastern United States showing areas visited during the Ivory-billed Woodpecker investigation. See table of areas for key to map.

summarized in the following table. For each area is given its name and general location, the date or dates it was visited, a short description of the type of country, what led to its being investigated, and what in brief was found there. The areas which are printed in italics in this table are treated more extensively in the succeeding section, 'Survey of Present Ivory-billed Woodpecker Populations and Localities.'

TABLE OF AREAS, KEY TO MAP, FIG. 12

South Carolina

1. *Pee Dee River Bottom*, Horry and Georgetown Cos.; Dec. 12–14, 1938; there is a small area of uncut tupelo swamp near the lower end of the river, not suitable for Ivory-bills, and I could find no reports of Ivory-bills being there.
2. *Steward's Neck–Wadmacaun section of the Santee Bottoms*, Georgetown Co.; July 19–24, Dec. 1–11, 1937; Nov. 27–Dec. 11, 1938; Ivory-bills have been observed several times in recent years in this section, a fairly large area of virgin tupelo and mixed swamp, but there were no signs of any of the birds residing in that area (see succeeding section).
3. *Santee Bottom, Wee Tee Lake section*, Williamsburg Co.; Dec. 16–18, 1938; a fairly large area of virgin sweet gum and oak swamp, now (1939) being logged, is fairly well suited to Ivory-bills, but I found no sign of the birds there.
4. *Black Oak Island section of the Santee Bottoms*, Clarendon Co.; Dec. 23, 1938; June 19–23, Nov. 29–Dec. 7, 1939; this is the best section for Ivory-bills of the whole Santee Bottoms, a large and excellent virgin forest of sweet gum and oaks, just now being logged (1939), where there have been old reports of Ivory-bills and where I found some possible but no positive sign of the birds (see succeeding section).
5. *Groton Plantation*, Hampton Co.; Jan. 14–17, 1937; here is a medium-sized area (7000 acres) of uncut mixed bottomland swamp along the Savannah River, but no reports or signs of Ivory-bills.

6. *Savannah River Waterfowl Refuge;* Jan. 18–19, 1937; June 17, 1939; an Ivory-bill was reported there in 1936 (Kubichek), but the record never was confirmed and the only swamp nearby is of small cypress trees, unsuitable.

Georgia

7. *Canoochee River*, Bryan Co.; June 15–16, 1939; an Ivory-bill was reported seen in the small swampy woods on the Canoochee, but after visiting the woods, looking at the sign, and listening to the observer, Mannie Carter, I decided the bird seen was a Pileated.

8. *Altamaha River Bottoms;* Jan. 20–25, 1937; a typical bottomland forest, which is almost completely cut over, for which I was not able to find any recent Ivory-bill reports or any sign.

9. *Okefenokee Wildlife Refuge;* June 19–23, 1939; Ivory-bills were formerly recorded there, and there have been some recent rumors, but Sam Mizell, who knows the birds, has seen none since 1912 even though he has been in the swamp continually, and none of the swamp I saw, mostly pond cypress, looked suitable for them.

Florida

10. *Vicinity of Oklawaha River and Ocala National Forest;* Feb. 19–23, 1937; Ivory-bills were formerly seen there, but there have been no recent reports and the swamp areas have been completely cut over, leaving no suitable habitat.

11. *Fort Christmas region*, eastern Orange Co.; Feb. 16–17, 1937; Feb. 17–18, 1939; several creek swamps of cypress and mixed timber border the St. John's River, intersecting pineland, and there have been reports of Ivory-bills seen there as late as 1936, but not since then and the swamps are now almost completely cut over.

12. *Jane Green swamp*, Brevard Co.; Feb. 19, 1939; I visited the swamp because of an Ivory-bill report, but found that it was based on a Pileated and that the swamp, of cut-over, mixed timber, was not very suitable for woodpeckers.

13. *Highlands Hammock State Park*, Highlands Co.; Dec. 31, 1938–Jan. 2, Feb. 11, 1939; Ivory-bills were seen in a small deadening near the park by O. E. Baynard late in 1937, but I could find no signs of the bird during my visit; the circumstances are described in the succeeding section.

14. *Big Cypress region*, Collier and Hendry Cos.; Feb. 6–13, 1937; Jan. 3–Feb. 9, 1939; this, one of the largest primitive areas in southern states, of mixed and varied swamps, has had several recent Ivory-bill reports; the details are described in the following section.

15. *Royal Palm Park*, Dade Co.; Feb. 3–4, 1937; Pileateds were mistaken for Ivory-bills there several years ago, and the hammock is too small and the

surrounding country without suitable timber for Ivory-bills to live there.

16. *Green swamp*, Polk Co.; Feb. 13–15, 1939; Ivory-bills were formerly recorded from this swamp, a region of cypress heads and swampy pine woods, but all of it has been repeatedly and recently cut over, and I found neither any suitable territory nor indications of the birds being there.

17. *Indian House Hammock*, near Richloam, Sumter Co.; March 4–5, 1937; an Ivory-bill was recently rumored seen here, a hammock and swamp along a small creek, but the suitable territory is so small that there is little or no chance of Ivory-bills being there.

18. *Gulf Hammock*, Levy Co.; Feb. 24–26, 1937; Mar. 2–3, 1939; this is the largest hammock in Florida, with a great variety of forest growth; there have been frequent rumors of Ivory-bills being there, and although I found no sign of the birds, nor any good timber not cut over, there is some possibility of a very few birds being there (see following section).

19. *Suwannee swamp and hammock*, Levy Co.; Feb. 23–28, 1939; there are small areas of hammock and swamp timber still uncut and occasional rumors of birds being seen, which is possible even though I found no sign of them.

20. *Lower Suwannee River and California swamp*, Dixie Co.; Feb. 26–27, Mar. 8–9, 1937; this was once a famous region for Ivory-bills, but the cypress swamps which were their habitat are all but completely cut over, and I found no indications of the birds.

21. *Bear Bay*, Dixie Co.; Mar. 10–11, 1939; this is a medium-sized area of virgin cypress swamp that is suitable for Ivory-bills although small; there are some rumors of birds being seen near there, but none are confirmed (see following section).

22. *Wacissa River region*, Jefferson Co.; Mar. 7–9, 1939; Ivory-bills were once reported to have been relatively common there, and were known by J. B. Royalls to be there, in the swamp of cypress, black gum, and other hardwoods until 1937, but he has not seen any since then, and now the swamp is completely logged over and I found no signs of the birds.

23. *Wakulla Resettlement Project*, now Wakulla National Forest; Mar. 12–15, 1937; Ivory-bills were reliably reported seen there in 1936 and early 1937 by George Van Hyning, who was the biologist for the resettlement project, in a large area of swampy pineland with many bays; I found some possible feeding sign there but no definite indications of birds residing. Several people working on the area watched for the birds but saw them no more.

24. *Apalachicola River Bottoms*, Gulf, Liberty, and Franklin Cos.; Mar. 14–17, May 30–June 7, 1939; the large area of tupelo swamp, still partly virgin, at the lower end of the river had some uncut ham-

mock adjoining it, and in this area I heard of some recent reports of Ivory-bills and found some possible feeding sign (see following sections).

25. *Near Panama City*, Bay Co.; Mar. 16, 1937; an Ivory-bill rumor from here was found to be based on Pileateds.

Alabama

26. *Tombigbee River Bottoms*, Sumter Co.; Feb. 14, 1938; near this area of partly uncut, mixed swamp timber there have been some recent Ivory-bill rumors, but in a brief examination I found no good territory nor anyone there who thought he had even seen the birds.

27. *Mobile Delta;* Aug. 23, 1938; this delta is a large swamp area of tupelo gum, now completely cut over, with no reports of Ivory-bills for many years.

Mississippi

28. *Pascagoula River swamp*, Jackson Co.; Aug. 22, 1938; May 26–27, 1939; Ivory-bills were formerly recorded seen there, but I found no part of this mixed swamp that was not cut over and at least two men who knew the swamp well were sure they had never seen any such birds.

29. *Pearl River Bottoms*, Miss. and La.; Aug. 19, 1938; I found these bottoms completely cut over, and know of no recent reports of Ivory-bills from there.

30. *Yazoo Delta*, Sharkey and Yazoo Cos.; June 20–22, 1938; there are two small tracts, including the DeSoto National Forest there, of virgin and partly virgin sweet gum and oak timber, but the suitable area is very small and in that I found no sign of the birds nor heard any reports of them.

Louisiana

31. *D'Arbonne swamp*, Ouachita Parish; May 22, 1939; a small cut-over swamp containing little but saplings where there have been some Ivory-bill rumors, but those I checked up on were based on Pileateds.

32. *Boeuf River Bottoms*, Ark. and La.; June 10–12, 16, 1938; Ivory-bills were recorded from there until about 1912, after which the timber was cut; now the bottoms are completely cut over, leaving no suitable territory, and I found no recent reports or signs of the birds.

33. *Tensas River Bottoms*, E. Carroll Parish; June 8–9, 13–15, 1938; Ivory-bills formerly ranged there, but the timber has since been all removed leaving no habitat for them, and I found no indications of birds still being there.

34. *Singer Tract*, Madison Parish; Mar. 21–July 15, Dec. 12–22, 1937; Feb. 15–June 6, June 24–29, Aug. 8–16, 1938; Mar. 23–May 25, 1939; the largest and best tract of virgin timber in the Mississippi Delta is here, where Ivory-bills have resided for many years; the findings in this tract are described in the following sections.

35. *Ayer's Tract*, Tensas Parish; June 15–16, 1937; June 30–July 1, 1938; Ivory-bills were formerly recorded from near the small area of virgin timber still remaining, but the territory is little suited to Ivory-bills; I found no signs, and men who know the birds have seen none in that area in many years.

36. *Black River Bottoms*, Concordia and Catahoula Parishes; June 29–30, 1937; July 1–2, 1938; there are some fairly large areas of virgin timber still remaining, but most is overcup oak flat, poor for Ivory-bills, and I found no indications of birds being there.

37. *West Feliciana Parish;* July 9, 1938; the Ivory-bill rumor from here was found to be based on Pileateds.

38. *Atchafalaya Basin*, Iberville, St. Martin, and Assumption Parishes; July 4–8, 1938; this is a very large swamp area, mostly of low overflow swamp, that is now completely cut over, and although there have been recent rumors of Ivory-bills seen there, I found no good territory and no one who had even possibly seen birds in recent years.

39. *Ponchatoula cypress swamp*, Tangipahoa Parish; July 7–9, 1937; the last large tract of cypress-gum swamp in Louisiana is here, but the habitat is poor for Ivory-bills and I found no possibility of the birds being there.

40. *Avery Island*, Iberia Parish; July 3, 1937; Ivory-bills were formerly recorded from here, and there have been some recent reports, but I examined the swamp where they were reported seen and found it to be small and cut over, the remaining trees being mostly tupelo, and no part of the area I saw being suitable for the birds.

Arkansas

41. *White River Waterfowl Refuge*, and vicinity, Arkansas and Desha Cos.; June 17–18, Aug. 1–6, 1938; Ivory-bills were once recorded from this area, and there are a few virgin tracts of sweet gum and oak timber but too small and scattered to make really good Ivory-bill territory; I found no indications of the birds still being there.

Texas

42. *Sulphur River Bottoms*, Cass Co.; July 30, 1938; I visited this area only because it was reported to be a tract of virgin timber, but it has been partly cut over and is a very poor type for Ivory-bills.

43. *Caddo Lake*, Harrison and Marion Cos.; July 29, 1938; the Ivory-bill rumors from there were undoubtedly based on Pileateds, for I found no suitable territory at all for the larger bird.

44. *Big Thicket*, Polk, Hardin, and Tyler Cos.; July 14–16, 23–26, 1938; this is low country of mixed pine and swampy forest, thoroughly logged over, and greatly over-rated as a wilderness area; there have been several reports of Ivory-bills being seen

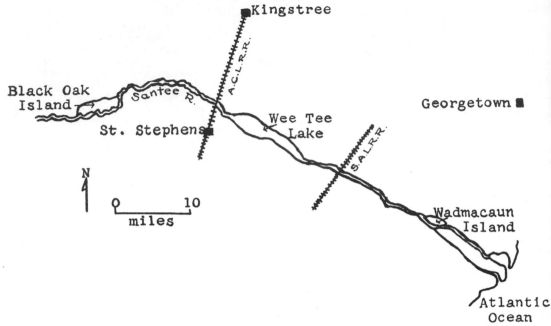

Fig. 13.   Map of Santee region, South Carolina.

in that region, but all the reports that I could check upon were based on the misidentification of the Pileateds.

45. *Bunn's Bluff vicinity*, Orange Co.; July 18–19, 1938; an Ivory-bill report was based on Pileateds, seen near a small uncut pine and hardwood hammock.

Forty-five areas were visited and investigated, besides several that were examined very briefly. Of these forty-five localities, six were investigated because of recent and reliable records of Ivory-bills, nineteen because of older records of those birds, ten because of Ivory-bill rumors based upon the misidentification of Pileateds, and ten because of the presence of virgin timber tracts alone.

Visits to these areas and the findings there have been described more thoroughly than in the above summary in a series of reports made on the progress of the fellowship study to the National Audubon Society.

Survey of Present Ivory-billed Woodpecker Populations and Localities

Santee River region, S. C. (see map, Fig. 13).—

A few years prior to 1935, George Melamphy reported Ivory-bills in the lower Santee swamps, and in 1935 the report was verified by Lester Walsh and Alexander Sprunt, Jr., who saw Ivory-bills in the Wadmacaun Island section, Georgetown County. From then through the winter of 1936–37 the birds were observed regularly, but in December 1937, a hunt was made in that area by myself and others and no Ivory-bills were found, and none have been reliably reported in that area since then.

In hunting through that area I found no signs that would indicate that Ivory-bills had ever resided steadily there, nothing such as roost holes or extensive feeding sign. The years that Ivory-bills were observed in the Wadmacaun Island section were good mast and berry years, and the birds were seen feeding upon gum berries. The following years were poor mast years. These facts taken together indicate that Ivory-bills never did reside steadily in the Wadmacaun Island section, but probably came to feed when the food was abundant there.

In late 1938 a rumor came that Ivory-bills had been seen on Black Oak Island, Clarendon County. This report was not verified, but a reliable account was received from W. M. Ridgill, of Manning, that Ivory-bills were in that section at least until about 1935. The Black Oak Island section proved to have the most suitable timber or forest for Ivory-bills, and I found some woodpecker work there in 1939 that looked much like the work of Ivory-bills, but none of it fresh nor in great amount.

To summarize: Ivory-bills were observed by reliable observers in different parts of the Santee swamp up until a few years ago, but never regularly and consistently in any one locality. Likewise, I did not find in any part of the swamp enough Ivory-bill sign to indicate that birds were residing steadily in one place. The simplest conclusion to draw from these facts is that there were a few birds in the Santee that moved around, choosing the best place for temporarily feeding and living, never staying long in one locality. The Black Oak Island section was probably the best suited area and the one they used the most.

Judged from the carrying capacity of the region, the number of Ivory-bills in the Santee swamp a few years ago did not exceed six individuals. Now, with the recent and present (1939) logging operations, which are reducing the size of suitable range, and the absence of recent reports of the birds, the numbers and even presence of the Ivory-bill in the Santee swamp is conjectural.

Big Cypress area, Fla. (see map, Fig. 14).— The last definite record by a recognized ornithologist for an Ivory-bill in the Big Cypress region is for 1914 by F. H. Kennard, who collected one at that time near Deep Lake. Since then there have been several rumors of the birds, which seem plausible because of the virgin and primitive condition of the Big Cypress, one of the last real wildernesses of the country.

Sheriff J. Thorpe, of Everglades, states that he saw Ivory-bills in 1937 near East Crossing, which is near the southern end of Main Strand. Charlie Billie, a Seminole in whom natives have confidence, gave a seemingly authentic account of seeing one Ivory-bill in 1938 at East Henson, a few miles from the preceding locality; he recog-

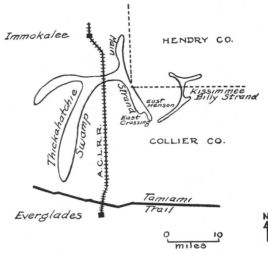

Fig. 14. Map of Big Cypress region, Florida.

nized the bird from a picture. Several other natives of the region remembered seeing Ivory-bills in earlier years and in various localities.

I spent considerable time hunting in the areas mentioned and in other parts of the Big Cypress, but found no sign of Ivory-bills. It may be that sign cannot be relied upon in the Big Cypress as it can in Louisiana and other more northern areas. Both F. H. Kennard (1915) and Robert Ridgway (1898) had difficulty finding Ivory-bills in the Big Cypress, so that my failure to find any birds does not eliminate the possibility of their being there.

Swamps in the Big Cypress were good for woodpeckers, and Pileateds were common. The occasional reports of Ivory-bills being seen and the size and primitive conditions of the area are the best indications that the birds are still present. In my opinion Ivory-bills very probably are there.

Ivory-bills have also been reported in recent years from the Shark River region of Florida, by J. M. Roberts of Punta Gorda (verbal), James Stanley of Miami (epist.), and others, but none of these reports have been investigated and I myself know nothing about the suitability of that country.

An estimate of the possible numbers of Ivory-bills in the Big Cypress can be based only upon the size of the areas and their suitability for the

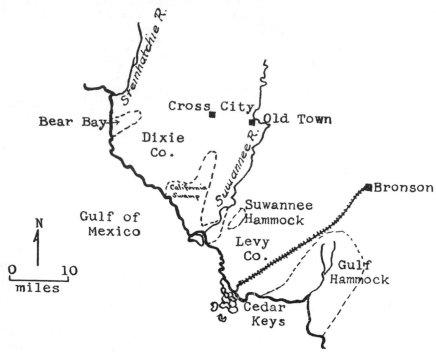

Fig. 15. Map of Gulf Hammock-Suwannee River region, Florida.

woodpeckers. In the southern part of the Main Strand there appears to be ample range for two pairs of Ivory-bills, and in the Thickahatchie swamp for at least two other pairs, making an estimate of a possible eight Ivory-bills for the Big Cypress area.

Western central Florida.—Oscar E. Baynard, of the Florida Park Service, reported (1937, and verbal) seeing Ivory-bills during the fall and early winter of 1937 in a small swamp adjacent to Highlands Hammock State Park. At the time he saw them there was some recently killed cypress in the swamp, and it was in this 'deadening' that Mr. Baynard saw the birds. The Ivory-bills have not been seen since then; the cypress stubs have dried out and few woodpeckers were feeding upon them when I visited the area early in 1939. The Ivory-bills probably moved off to better feeding grounds, wherever that might have been.

Gulf Hammock–Suwannee region, Fla. (see map, Fig. 15).—From Gulf Hammock westward along the Gulf coast there is a largely uninhabited, swampy country covering hundreds of square miles. Formerly Ivory-bills were recorded more commonly in this region than elsewhere; now almost all of it has been logged over and there are few really good woods left for the birds. In the areas that I hunted I found no signs of Ivory-bills, but several natives reported seeing them within recent years, and it is probable that some Ivory-bills are still present. The territory is very large, and there are some small tracts of virgin and nearly inaccessible timber still standing. A fair estimate of the number of Ivory-bills in the large area is two pairs, or four individuals.

Apalachicola River bottoms, Fla. (see map, Fig. 16).—The Apalachicola region ranks just below the Santee in the amount of virgin bottomland timber still standing. There are two large tracts of virgin timber along the lower part of the river, and both of them, but especially the lower one, along Brother's River, present good

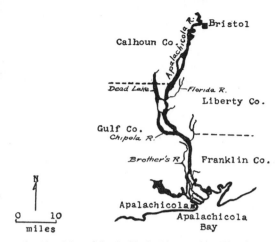

Fig. 16.   Map of Apalachicola River region, Florida.

in the Mississippi Delta and is remarkable in that it is inhabited by almost every animal and bird native to that region, except those that are now extinct. Most of the Ivory-bill study was carried on in this tract, and because of the amount of material gathered, the history of the Ivory-bills in this tract is presented in later sections.

In the spring of 1939, I located in the tract one pair of Ivory-bills with their single young of that year, one young male raised by that same pair in 1938, and another solitary male. In addition I observed definite Ivory-bill sign that was done by another bird or birds, and judging from the reports of natives, probably by a single male bird. This makes a total of six birds, including one breeding pair. There is a possibility of another pair having been present, reported by natives, but neither I nor my assistant, Jesse Laird, could find any definite sign of them. Eight birds would be the maximum Ivory-bill population in the Singer Tract in the spring of 1939, with six the probable number.

On a short trip to the Singer Tract in December 1941, I found that the number of Ivory-bills had changed little or not at all since 1939.

TABULATION OF THE LOCATIONS AND PROBABLE NUMBERS OF IVORY-BILLED WOODPECKERS IN 1939

Locality	Number of individuals	Basis for estimate of numbers
Santee region, S. C.	?	. . . .
Big Cypress area, Fla.	6	Estimate based on carrying capacity of region and locations of reports
West-central Fla.	2	Known to be there in late 1937 by O. E. Baynard
Gulf Hammock–Suwannee region, Fla.	4	Estimates based on carrying capacity of region
Apalachicola region, Fla.	4	Estimates based on carrying capacity of region and reports of natives
Singer Tract, La.	6	Five individuals observed and sign of at least one other individual
Approximate total	22	

habitat for woodpeckers. The lower part of the Apalachicola swamp has been almost completely neglected by competent naturalists and ornithologists and very little is known about it.

Several natives and hunters in that region have reported seeing Ivory-bills, some of them knowing the birds and some satisfactorily describing them. Reports that I judge to be reliable are for four different localities in the lower part of the river. Two of these are in or near the lower tract of virgin timber, and in this tract I found some feeding sign and holes that looked like the work of Ivory-bills. Although there was not enough sign to be positive evidence, its presence added weight to the statements of the natives.

I do not feel that an adequate search of the area has yet been made; for at the time I visited the area, in June, it was a poor season to hunt for Ivory-bills and I could not secure the proper equipment, boat and motor, to reach all sections.

As in the case of other areas, the numbers of Ivory-bills likely to be in the region can only be estimated by the size and suitability of the region. There is adequate range for two pairs, or four individuals, in the lower part of the Apalachicola swamp, and the rather wide distribution of the natives' reports indicates that at least that many are there.

Singer Tract, Madison Parish, La.—The Singer Tract is the largest tract of virgin timber

Part III.   Ecology of the Ivory-billed Woodpecker

THE knowledge needed for successful conservation of the Ivory-billed Woodpecker will come in greatest part from the study of the ecology of the species, of the relations between the woodpecker and its environment, for we are able to control many factors in the environment. This study examines how the Ivory-bill lives—in relation to other Ivory-bills and other kinds of life, how it secures food, which factors benefit and which harm the species. The existence of any kind of animal depends upon two elements: the success in living of the individuals, and the reproductive success of the individuals; this is a study of the first.

CHAPTER 6

Population Density and Individual Range

NONE of the earlier accounts of the Ivory-billed Woodpecker contained accurate or definite statements as to the abundance of the bird. Judging from the interest that naturalists and collectors had in the Ivory-bill, and the accounts they wrote, it never was common. Most writers mentioned the Ivory-bill as being a rare bird, or an uncommon one, and some heightened this picture by describing the difficulties they had in securing specimens.

The one exception to this is a statement by Audubon (1842) that the Ivory-bill was "very abundant" along the Buffalo Bayou (near Houston ?), Texas; he procured several specimens there. But the words "very abundant" have little meaning alone; the Ivory-bill may have been abundant there compared with other birds or compared with the number of Ivory-bills in other localities. Audubon usually described the big woodpecker as being quite rare.

A better estimate of the population density of the bird can be secured from a study of the Ivory-billed Woodpecker in certain localities. A. T. Wayne collected during the springs of 1892, 1893, and 1894 in northern Florida in the Suwannee and Wacissa River regions, and one objective of his collecting was the Ivory-bill. His field catalogue, now kept at the Charleston Museum, furnished most of the following information. In 1892, he or his hunters killed five Ivory-bills in California swamp, an area of about sixty square miles lying southwest of Old Town, Fla., and he saw four additional birds there several days after the fifth bird was collected. The following year, 1893, five more Ivory-bills were collected from that swamp.

During my own visit to that area, in 1937, I talked with some natives who remembered collecting for Wayne, and gathered from them that after Wayne's work there Ivory-bills were very unusual and that he had secured almost all of them. Ten birds were collected from California swamp in two years; since that was probably almost all the birds in that swamp, the total population was once probably about twelve individuals, or six pairs of Ivory-bills in the sixty square miles of swamp.

In 1894, Wayne collected in the Wacissa and Aucilla River region, and between February 12 and April 30 of that year he secured nineteen Ivory-bills from the swamps of the Wacissa River. It is probable that some Ivory-bills were left there as a few did persist in that region until about 1937. The Wacissa swamps cover an area of about seventy-five square miles and, estimating a population of about twenty-five individuals, before Wayne's collecting, there were probably about twelve pairs of Ivory-bills in that seventy-five square miles.

Wayne's writing would indicate that Ivory-bills were more common in those localities than do the data from his field catalogue. Of the Wacissa region, he states (1895) that Ivory-bills were once common in that region and already, at the time of his collecting, were rapidly becoming extinct. He also states (1910) that he saw two

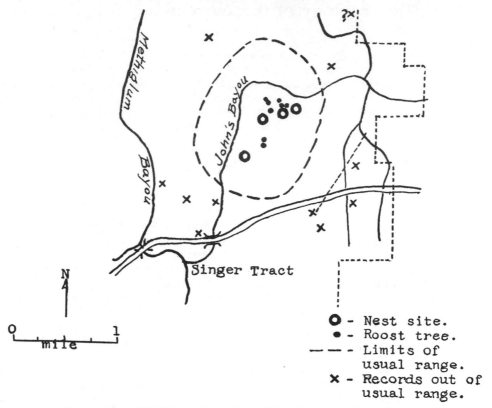

O - Nest site.
● - Roost tree.
— — - Limits of
       usual range.
✗ - Records out of
     usual range.

Fig. 17.   Ivory-billed Woodpecker territory, John's Bayou area, Singer Tract, La.

hundred Ivory-bills in Florida during the years 1892 to 1894. Some of these were undoubtedly repeated observations of the same individuals. During this time he entered in his field catalogue data for forty-four Ivory-bill specimens, many of which were collected by local hunters.

The Singer Tract in Louisiana contained about 120 square miles of virgin forest in 1934, and during that year there were about seven pairs of Ivory-bills on the tract, the largest population for any year I estimated.

This gives three estimates of the abundance or density of Ivory-bills in primitive areas: in Louisiana, seven pairs in 120 square miles or one pair per seventeen square miles; in California swamp in northern Florida, about six pairs in sixty square miles or one pair per ten square miles; in the Wacissa swamps in northern Florida, about

twelve pairs in seventy-five square miles or one pair per six and a quarter square miles. The last figure is probably close to the maximum density, for in the Singer Tract a pair of Ivory-bills in the nesting season ranged over from three to four square miles.

While in the Singer Tract, I attempted to make an estimate of the numbers of other species of woodpeckers in that area. The estimate was made by counting all the woodpeckers observed or heard within a certain distance of the route I was traveling at the time, computing the area covered in that way, and then calculating the density.

It was not a very satisfactory way as the results obtained from individual counts varied considerably even for the same area, but the averages of several counts did show quite uniform results- From this estimate the density of Pileated Wood.

Plate 7. Ivory-bill feeding sign on dead locust trees.

Plate 8. Ivory-bill feeding sign on slender limb.

Plate 9. Dead young pine trees scaled of their bark by an Ivory-bill.

Plate 10. Beetle larvae from beneath bark of Nuttall's oak.

peckers in the Singer Tract was six pairs per square mile and the density of Red-bellied Woodpeckers was about twenty-one pairs per square mile.

Counts were made in the same way in other areas that I visited to get some concept of the abundance of Pileated Woodpeckers in different habitats. Too few counts were made in each area to be considered accurate, but the following figures were obtained for the density of Pileated Woodpeckers (probably not all breeding birds): Santee River bottoms, S.C.—ten individuals per square mile; swamps of northern Florida— twelve individuals per square mile; Big Cypress swamp, Fla.—twelve individuals per square mile. They all equal or come close to the density of Pileateds in the Singer Tract.

Considering the maximum abundance of the Ivory-bill to have been one pair per six square miles, of the Pileated to be six pairs per one square mile, and of the Red-bellied to be twenty-one pairs per one square mile, the relative abundance of these birds would be one Ivory-bill to thirty-six Pileated to 126 Red-bellied Woodpeckers.

Range of Individual Ivory-bills

The pair of Ivory-billed Woodpeckers that have been most studied inhabited the John's Bayou area of the Singer Tract, Louisiana. The range of this pair was worked out by repeated observations and following of the birds, and is shown on the map, Fig. 17. The roosting area was the center of the range, for they returned there to roost almost every night and traveled in any direction from there for feeding during the day, usually confining their travels to the best areas. During the nesting season, the pair rarely, if ever, exceeded the limits of their usual range, shown by the long dashed lines, but after the young were large enough to travel well they often went beyond their usual range. The dotted line connecting two 'x's means that those two records were for the same day; in this case the birds were followed that distance, from one spot to the other. The usual range of this pair of Ivory-bills was from three-quarters to one mile from the roosting ground, while the greatest distance that they have been

observed from the roosting ground is about one and one-half miles. These records are for the nesting and summer season.

In the Mack's Bayou area of the Singer Tract there lived a single male bird during the 1938 and 1939 seasons. Judging from the extra white on his primaries, I believed him to be a young bird (see section describing juvenal plumage); his unusual wing pattern made it easy to identify him, and in 1938 his voice had a peculiar timbre, 'his head in a bucket' sound, and both J. J. Kuhn and I were able to recognize him every time by his voice. The map, Fig. 18, shows his range. Only one roosting hole was found, but he probably had others, as some nights he did not appear at that tree. As can be seen from the records spotted on the map, he traveled widely, but not enough observations were made to be able to state accurately his usual range; the extreme record was for two and a half miles from the roost hole, which he was using regularly at the time. The woods between the roost hole and this spot were poor feeding grounds for Ivory-bills. The traveling of almost two miles, shown by the dotted line, was done between 8 A.M. and 2 P.M. on April 30, 1938.

The range shown for the Ivory-bills in these two areas of the Singer Tract is their spring and early summer range. I have tried to follow the John's Bayou pair in the winter, but they traveled so fast that I was unable to keep up with them after they had left the roost, and at the rate they traveled they seemed intent on going some distance. That the winter range is probably larger than the summer is indicated by an observation made by J. J. Kuhn. On December 19, 1937, about 7:30 A.M., he found three Ivory-bills, a male and two females, and followed them until late morning when he lost them; they were then two miles from the spot where he had first found them and had traveled in a semicircle of at least three and a half miles in about four hours.

The studies of Ivory-bills made in the Singer Tract might indicate that the birds use the same range year after year, that they are sedentary, with ranges up to four miles or more across. The John's Bayou birds, whose range has been described, have been quite sedentary, for I believe the same pair has used that territory for at least

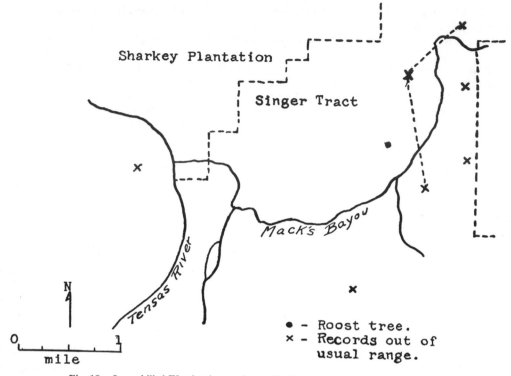

Fig. 18.   Ivory-billed Woodpecker territory, Mack's Bayou area, Singer Tract, La.

three years. On the other hand, pairs of birds and individuals, especially young birds, have disappeared from the Singer Tract, and the simplest explanation is that they have wandered away, for there was no evidence of their having been killed either by predators or by shooting. Predators would rarely get both members of a pair, and it was almost always a pair of birds that disappeared.

The only definite observations made in that vicinity of apparently wandering birds were by J. J. Kuhn in September 1937. Fishing early in the morning, he saw three Ivory-bills apparently leave a roost in some cypress trees bordering a small lake about ten miles north of the Singer Tract, and he watched them fly off. The country surrounding the lake for several miles is completely cut over, unsuited for Ivory-bills or almost any kind of woodpecker. I visited the area the follow-

ing spring and found no place suitable for Ivory-bills and no birds roosting around the same lake. It seems likely that Mr. Kuhn happened to see a trio of wandering birds.

There are other Ivory-bill records that seem to have been made on wandering birds. In 1866, W. C. Avery (1890) killed a female Ivory-bill in Hale County, Alabama, the only occurrence known to him of Ivory-bills being in that country. C. W. Howe, a trapper, killed one near Troy, Alabama (Howell, 1907), the only one he ever saw in the state. George Van Hyning saw a pair of Ivory-bills in southwestern Leon County, Florida, in June 1936, and again in January 1937, but could not find them at other times nor could other persons. The Ivory-bills seen at Highlands Hammock State Park (Baynard, 1937) suddenly appeared for a few months, during fall and winter, and then disappeared. In the lower Santee region of South Carolina, Ivory-bills were observed quite regularly from 1935 to 1937, although there were no signs of their roosting or nesting there, but neither the birds nor signs of them could be found in late 1937 or 1938.

Attempting to find more evidence for either a sedentary or non-sedentary habit in Ivory-bills, I measured as many Ivory-bill specimens, eighty-eight, as I could. I assumed that if Ivory-bills were sedentary, the birds of one locality would show little variation in the length of the bill and wing as compared with the variations of these measurements on birds taken over a large area, since the birds of one locality would have been isolated by a sedentary habit and inbred to a more uniform size. Non-sedentary birds should not show any such condition as their wandering would prevent segregation, for example, of long or short-billed types. Florida specimens yielded the most data because more birds have been collected from that state. The standard deviation from the mean was used as a measure of the variation of the lengths. A table of measurements of bill lengths follows; the length of the bill was preferred because the bill is not subject to seasonal wear as is the wing.

BILL LENGTHS OF FLORIDA IVORY-BILLED WOODPECKERS

Bill Lengths of Males

Locality	Number of specimens	Mean length, mm.	Standard deviation, mm.
All of Florida	38	74.0	2.8
Jefferson Co.	3	76.4	3.0
Dixie Co.	3	72.7	2.4
Rosewood, Levy Co.	3	72.2	3.8
Sanford vicinity	3	75.0	3.6
Punta Rassa	4	76.7	1.8
Big Cypress	3	72.1	0.8

Bill Lengths of Females

All of Florida	38	70.1	2.8
Jefferson Co.	3	72.2	1.6
Dixie Co.	3	69.9	1.8
Rosewood, Levy Co.	3	68.1	4.3
Sanford vicinity	5	69.2	0.8
Punta Rassa	5	70.6	3.2
Big Cypress	3	69.6	3.2

Male Ivory-bills from three localities showed less variation in bill length than did males from all

over Florida, while males from the other three localities showed greater than the state-wide variation. The bills of females showed the same thing, that three of the six females had less and three had more variation than the state-wide variation. Only two of the localities showed the same condition for both sexes. The wing measurements are likely to be more variable because of feather wear, but they behaved the same as the bill measurements—for both sexes three of the localities showed less variation than for the whole state and three showed more. Although the evidence is not conclusive, the large variation that occurred in half of the samples of Ivory-bills from one locality indicates that the Ivory-bills have not been sedentary there and have not inbred to a standard size for that locality.

Considering all the evidence, I believe that Ivory-bills were not sedentary birds, but sometimes wandered considerable distances. Some of the birds in the Singer Tract have remained in one locality for a few to several years, but there they are almost confined by the cut-over condition of the surrounding country. There are records in Louisiana, Florida, and South Carolina which can be most easily explained as being observations of wandering birds. The measurements of specimens from Florida frequently show much variation in birds from one locality, which would not be expected if the birds were sedentary for many years in a limited area.

Evidence will be presented later, in the chapter on 'The Effect of Quantity of Food on the Distribution of the Ivory-billed Woodpecker,' to show that their wandering and ranges are probably controlled by the abundance of food. These birds apparently require an unusually large supply of certain wood-boring insects, their main food, and because of certain conditions, these insects are abundant only in occasional localities and for a comparatively short time. Ivory-bills will usually remain in one locality as long as there is an adequate food supply, but when that decreases they may have to move for considerable distances until they can find another suitable area. Many species of woodpecker are considered sedentary, but it is well known that they will move into areas where a large amount of timber has been killed, affording abundant food for them, and they will leave when that supply diminishes. Ivory-bills behave in the same way, but because they seem to require a large quantity of certain borers that sometimes fluctuate greatly in numbers, they probably move more often and farther than other species.

Furthermore, the Ivory-bill is well adapted to traveling for long distances. It is a strong flier with a fast flight for a woodpecker, and individuals have been observed feeding over several square miles. They usually travel in pairs, the two birds moving closely together, which would be important for wandering birds of few numbers in order that mates may keep together.

CHAPTER 7

History of the Ivory-billed Woodpecker Population in the Singer Tract

THE Singer Tract, Madison Parish, Louisiana, has for several years been known as a locality for Ivory-billed Woodpeckers; much more useful and important information about the bird has been obtained in that area than in any other, and so the known facts about the history of the tract and of its Ivory-bill population are assembled here.

The earliest record for Ivory-bills in Madison Parish is for 1891, a specimen in the American Museum of Natural History collected by E. M. Haskell. In 1899 George E. Beyer (1900) found Ivory-bills in northern Franklin Parish, in an area about six miles from the Singer Tract. Mason Spencer, of Tallullah, now middle-aged, learned to hunt as a boy in the woods that are now the Singer Tract, and remembers having his father point out Ivory-bills. Knowledge of the birds' presence there became widespread when Mr. Spencer collected a single male Ivory-bill in April 1932, for the Louisiana Department of Conservation. Hearing of this report, Dr. T. Gilbert Pearson and Ernest G. Holt visited the tract in May 1932, and succeeded in observing about six birds. Since that time several people have visited the area for observing, studying, or photographing the Ivory-bills, and it has received more attention than any other area. There have been several local people interested in the birds, especially J. J. Kuhn, who for several years served as an agent for the State Conservation Department in the Singer Tract, and these people helped many times by supplying information about the Ivory-bills.

The forest on the Singer Tract has been very little touched by man. Some of the early settlers along the Tensas River cleared land along the river banks for cotton fields. The largest of these old plantations had about 3000 acres under cultivation. Almost all of these old fields were abandoned during or soon after the Civil War and reverted to forest growth. The property changed hands several times, until the present tract was acquired by the Singer Manufacturing Company about 1916. The area was hunted heavily until about 1920, when the tract became a wildlife sanctuary maintained by the state of Louisiana, and hunting was prohibited. The tract contains about 80,000 acres, over four-fifths of which was virgin timber at the time this Ivory-bill study began. In 1937 logging rights on the western half of the tract were sold to the Chicago Mill and Lumber Company, and they started logging there in 1938. About the same time the Tendal Lumber Company acquired rights and started logging at the northern edge of the tract. In 1939 rights to the rest of the tract were purchased by the Chicago Mill and Lumber Company, and logging on the eastern side began in 1941.

Those who have known this area for many years, such as the old hunters, cowmen, and wardens, claim that Ivory-bills were once quite common in the tract, more numerous than in recent years. Some of these reports can be disregarded, especially those which report the Ivory-bills as having been more common than the Pileated Woodpecker. Many of the reports made by reliable people were overestimates, because they assumed that Ivory-bills had a much smaller range than is actually true. Some of these people, however, could remember clearly when and where they used to see Ivory-bills in the tract, and the reports of different individuals usually checked with each other. Studying these reports carefully, I have been able to make what I consider a fairly reliable estimate of the numbers of Ivory-bills in the tract since 1934. The estimates for the years 1934 and 1936 are based entirely on the reports of others. In 1935 and in 1937 through 1939, my own observations supplemented by those of others were used in making the estimates.

For purposes of describing the history and changes of the Ivory-bill population, the tract can be divided into several Ivory-bill areas. These areas are not sharply defined units, but are parts of the woods where the forest is well suited to the birds, usually separated from other similar areas by less suitable forest. In the recent history of the tract, Ivory-bills have almost always ranged in

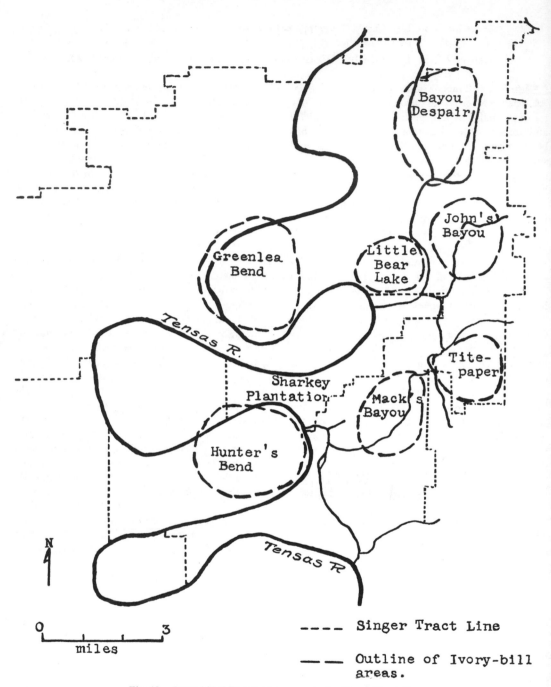

Bayou
Despair

John's
Bayou

Greenlea
Bend

Little
Bear
Lake

Tensas R.

Tite-
paper

Sharkey
Plantation

Mack's
Bayou

Hunter's
Bend

Tensas R.

N

0   3
miles

- - - - Singer Tract Line

──── Outline of Ivory-bill
areas.

Fig. 19. Ivory-billed Woodpecker areas in the Singer Tract, La.

these areas. The map of the Singer Tract, Fig. 19, shows the location of these and their names.

TABLE OF IVORY-BILL POPULATION IN THE SINGER TRACT 1934–1939

Abbreviations: pr. = pair; m. = male adult; yg. = young or juvenal

Italics indicate presence of these birds known from my own observations; others were observed by persons in whom I have confidence.

	1934	1935	1936
Bayou Despair	1 pr.	1 pr.	1 pr.
Greenlea Bend	1 pr.	?	?
John's Bayou	1 pr. & 2 yg.	*1 pr., nest*	1 pr. & 4 yg. & 1 pr.
Little Bear Lake	1 pr.	0	0
Titepaper	1 pr. & 2 yg.	?	1 pr. & 2 yg.
Mack's Bayou	1 pr.	*1 pr., nest*	1 pr.
Hunter's Bend	1 pr.	1 pr.	1 pr.
	7 pr. & 4 yg.	?	6 pr. & 6 yg.

	1937	1938	1939
Bayou Despair	1 pr. & 1 yg.	0	0
Greenlea Bend	*1 m.*	*1 m.*	*1 m.*
John's Bayou	*1 pr. & 1 yg. & 1 pr.*	*1 pr. & 1 yg.*	*1 pr. & 1 yg. & 1 m.*
Little Bear Lake	0	0	0
Titepaper & Mack's Bayou	1 pr.	1 pr. & 2 yg. & 1 m.	*1 m.*
Hunter's Bend	1 pr.	logged, 0	0
	5 pr. & 1 m. & 2 yg.	2 pr. & 2 m. & 3 yg.	1 pr. & 3 m. & 1 yg.

The population of Ivory-bills in the Singer Tract has shown a steady decrease since 1934. The only possible cause that I could find for this steady decline is an apparent decrease in the amount of woodpecker food available, thus limiting the number of birds that could inhabit the tract; this is described in the chapter 'The Effect of Quantity of Food on the Distribution of the Ivory-billed Woodpecker.' The decrease in numbers may have been accentuated by an unusually high number of Ivory-bills in the tract about 1934, due to an influx of birds from surrounding areas as these were logged over, forcing the Ivory-bills to retreat to the virgin timber in the Singer Tract; but this is mere speculation. There has been some evidence, but none of it conclusive, that Ivory-bills have been shot by poachers in the tract, shot more from curiosity than for any other reason. But the primary reasons for the decrease apparently are natural, and if interpreted correctly, will help to explain the ecology and the various requirements of the species.

CHAPTER 8

Food and Feeding Habits

THE kinds of food eaten by the Ivory-billed Woodpecker have been learned by numerous observations on feeding birds and from a few stomach examinations. The variety and exact identity of its food is not accurately known, for the surest way to identify kinds of food is by numerous stomach examinations, and this has not been possible because of the scarcity of the bird. Work in the field and perusal of many published records have, however, accumulated much information about the Ivory-bill's food habits.

The United States Fish and Wildlife Service has examined the stomach contents of three Ivory-billed Woodpeckers; the complete contents and percentage of each kind of food in each stomach is listed below with the data for each specimen (from files of the U. S. Fish and Wildlife Service):

Bowling Green, West Carroll Parish, La.,
August 19, 1903   E. L. Moseley
Animal matter 61%   Vegetable matter 39%

Fragment of 1 *Stenodontes dasystomus*		20%
"	" 2 *Parandra polita*	31
"	" larval Cerambycids	10
Undetermined gall fragment		1
43 seeds and plant fibers of *Rhus radicans*		38
Chips of wood and vegetable fragments		1

C. Cottam

Tarkington, Texas
Nov. 26, 1904   11 A.M.   V. Bailey
Stomach well filled
Animal matter 42%   Vegetable matter 58%

Remains of 7 or more Scolytid beetles, *Tomicus*	2%
About 20 Cerambycid larvae	40
Seeds of *Magnolia foetida*	42
Shell and meat of small hickory nut	16

F. E. Beal

Tarkington, Texas
Nov. 26, 1904   6 P.M.   V. Bailey
Stomach well filled
Animal matter 35%   Vegetable matter 65%

At least 32 Cerambycid larvae	35%
Remains of pecans	65

F. E. Beal

The contents of these three stomachs have been summarized by Cottam and Knappen (1939) as follows: 46% of combined contents was of animal origin, 45.33% being of long-horned beetles (Cerambycidae), and 0.67% was of engraver beetles, *Tomicus* sp.; 54% was of vegetable origin, 14% being of seeds of *Magnolia grandiflora*, 27% being of *Carya*, 12.67% being of seeds of poison ivy, and 0.33% being fragments of an unidentified gall.

Alexander Wilson (1811) wrote of some Ivory-bills he collected in the Carolina region: "In the stomachs of three which I opened, I found large quantities of a species of worm called borers, two or three inches long, of a dirty cream color, with a black head." This description fits some of the larger larval Cerambycidae very well. P. H. Gosse (1859) collected two Ivory-bills near Selma, Alabama, and found in the stomach of one a large "*Cerambyx*" and the stones of several cherries, and in another nothing but cherries.

In the debris that I obtained from an Ivory-bill nest in the Singer Tract, Madison Parish, Louisiana, soon after the young had left the nest, were the following remains from the food brought to the young Ivory-bill:

1   fragment of an Elaterid larvae.
18   mandibles of *Stenodontes dasystomus*, a Cerambycid.
3   mandibles resembling *Neoclytus capraea*, a Cerambycid.
1   mandible resembling *Dynastes tityrus*, a Scarabaeid.
(Mandibles identified by Henry Dietrich)
Few fragments of adult insects, probably Coleoptera.

The beetle mandibles found in the nest debris undoubtedly came from larvae, as beetle-like larvae were the food that I almost always observed brought to the nest. Large larvae resembling *Stenodontes dasystomus* were seen frequently carried in the bills of adult Ivory-bills, but not as frequently as smaller larvae, so the preponderance of mandibles of *Stenodontes* found in the nest must be due to their large size, smaller mandibles probably remaining imbedded in the feces and removed when the adults cleaned the nest.

Audubon (1831) describes the food of the Ivory-bill as being beetles, larvae, and large grubs, and also grapes, persimmons, and hackberries. E. A. McIlhenny (Bendire) states that Ivory-bills feed also upon acorns; and Alexander Sprunt, Jr., told me that in South Carolina he saw Ivory-bills feeding upon tupelo and black gum berries.

Wood-boring larvae are unquestionably the most important food of the Ivory-bill. In all of my observations in the Singer Tract I never saw Ivory-bills feed upon anything but such larvae, and that is all that Mr. Kuhn ever saw the birds eat. Probably the seasons that fruits or seeds are eaten is from late summer to early winter, when they are most available; the Ivory-bill stomachs that contained such a large percentage of vegetable food were collected in November.

Ivory-billed Woodpeckers do most of their feeding by scaling the bark from dead trunks and branches to secure the borers that live between the bark and the sapwood (Plates 7 and 8). In seventy percent of my observations of Ivory-bills' feeding in Louisiana, the birds were scaling the bark from the trees; the remainder of the time they fed by digging into the sap or heartwood for deeper-living borers. In these observations the woodpeckers were feeding on hardwood trees such as sweet gum and oaks, but A. A. Allen states (Allen and Kellogg) that he observed Ivory-bills feeding in Florida by scaling the bark from fire-killed pine trees (Plate 9). Audubon (1831) also describes Ivory-bills feeding by stripping the bark from trees.

The borers that live between the bark and the sapwood are mostly larval Coleoptera: Scolytids, Buprestids, and Cerambycids (Plate 10). They are the first to attack a tree or a limb after its death, mining in the inner bark, between the bark and sapwood, or in the extreme outer sapwood. As the bark loosens, the wood dries and softens, and the borers that live there mine deeper, gradually progressing from the outer sapwood through into the heartwood. As the Ivory-bills feed mostly on the borers between the bark and sapwood, they do most of their feeding on wood that has recently died, and in most of my observations the birds were feeding on limbs or trees so recently dead that the twigs had not yet fallen and the bark was hard and tight. As decay progresses in a tree, the Ivory-bills move downward with the progression of the 'shallow' borers, from the limbs to the trunk of a tree, so that in a quite recently dead tree the birds feed on the branches and smaller limbs while on one longer dead they feed on the trunk.

Ivory-bills feed energetically. They knock the bark loose with sidewise blows and quick flicks of the bill. The bark is usually quite tight, but the woodpeckers rapidly knock off pieces from the size of a silver dollar to the size of a man's hand; loose bark is detached in even larger pieces. They occasionally pry with their bills under the still-attached bark after the borers there. I have seen one quickly press its body close to the tree to catch borers that tumbled out as the bark was loosened, and then reach down with its bill to pick them up. They usually eat the borers as rapidly as they uncover and catch them, but in carrying food to the young they can hold a considerable number of borers in the mouth and the rear of the bill and still dig for and pick up more. Scaling, the Ivory-bill works steadily, removing all the bark for quite an area; one may work at a spot for an hour or more.

When Ivory-bills dig, they chisel into the sap and heartwood for borers like other woodpeckers, digging slightly conical holes that are usually circular in cross-section (Plate 11). They dig with unbelievable rapidity in soft wood like hackberry, chiseling out a hole five inches deep in less than a minute. Their strength was again demonstrated when I saw one dig to the center of a live oak limb five inches in diameter and also into a living oak trunk.

Ivory-bills in Louisiana usually feed high, in the dying tops of old trees, but they are not averse to coming close to the ground. A. A. Allen (Allen and Kellogg) describes a female Ivory-bill hopping about on the ground in Florida, and J. J. Kuhn observed an Ivory-bill in Louisiana digging at the base of a tree within a foot of the ground.

The kinds of trees that Ivory-bills fed upon most frequently in the Singer Tract are shown in the following table, which is a tabulation of my feeding observations. This table shows the number of observations made of Ivory-bills feeding on each species of trees, both scaling bark and digging, and the percentage of each. All the important species of trees present in the Singer Tract are listed, with their relative abundance in the forest expressed as a percentage of the total of trees one foot or more in diameter.

SUMMARY OF FEEDING OBSERVATIONS ON THE IVORY-BILLED WOODPECKER IN THE SINGER TRACT, LA., 1937–39

Tree Species	Rela-tive abun-dance[1]	No. of observa-tions		Percentage of total		Total[2]
		Scl	Dig	Scl	Dig	
Sweet gum	20.8	40	3	39.6	3.0	42.6
Nuttall's oak	10.6	20	7	19.8	6.9	26.7
Willow oak	6.4	1	0	1.0	0	1.0
Water oak	3.2	0	0	0	0	0
Overcup oak	8.9	1	3	1.0	3.0	4.0
Green ash	14.6	1	0	1.0	0	1.0
Hackberry	15.4	2	10	2.0	9.9	11.9
Red maple	2.7	1	1	1.0	1.0	2.0
American elm	10.2	2	1	2.0	1.0	3.0
Cedar elm	2.5	1	1	1.0	1.0	2.0
Pecan and water hickory	2.7	2	1	2.0	1.0	3.0
Honey locust	1.8	2	0	2.0	0	2.0
Persimmon	0.2	0	1	0	1.0	1.0
Bald cypress	0.2	0	0	0	0	0
	100.2	73	28	72.4	27.8	100.2

Scl—Feeding by scaling bark from trees
Dig—Feeding by digging into wood
[1] Relative abundance of tree species of forest expressed as percentage of total trees of one foot or more in diameter
[2] Total percentage of feeding observations for each tree species
(Scientific names of trees in Appendix)

The table shows that the Ivory-bills fed upon sweet gum and Nuttall's oak trees more than any other species, both in number of feedings and in proportion to the abundance of each species in the forest. Over 69% of their feeding was done on 31% of the forest, of which two-thirds was sweet gum (Plate 12) and one-third Nuttall's oak. Hackberry (Plate 11) was the only other tree fed on to a marked extent; the remainder of the feeding was scattered among other species of trees.

The table also shows how much of the Ivory-bill's feeding was done by scaling, about 72%. Hackberry and overcup oak were the only trees on which Ivory-bills did more digging than scaling.

The importance of sweet gum and Nuttall's oak trees to the Ivory-billed Woodpecker, at least in the Mississippi Delta, is further demonstrated by the range and distribution of the bird; it has always preferred parts of the forest where those trees were abundant, and throughout the Mississippi Delta it has inhabited areas where the sweet gum-oak type of forest stood. Ivory-bills prefer sweet gum and Nuttall's oak trees for feeding probably because those trees support a larger number of borers that live between the bark and the sapwood than do others. In collecting borers from beneath the bark of dead limbs and trees, I was able to find more in sweet gum and oak than in other species. Both of these trees have comparatively thin bark, and thin-barked trees always seemed to have more borers than kinds with thick bark. Pileated Woodpeckers, while they do little scaling after borers, do more on sweet gum than on any other tree (see following table of Pileated feeding).

The graph (Fig. 20) compares the frequency of Ivory-bill feeding on different kinds and sizes of trees with the abundance of the different kinds and sizes. Each black column shows the percentage of all the trees in the forest that are of a certain size and species, and the cross-hatched column shows the percentage of Ivory-bill feeding done on trees of that size and species. The sizes, diameter breast high, have been grouped into size classes, 3 to 12 inches, 13 to 24 inches, and so forth.

The composition of the forest stand was found by taking quarter-acre plots at random throughout the forest, and in each plot counting all the trees and classifying each tree as to species and size, diameter at breast height. The plots were circular, twenty yards in radius, which closely approximates a quarter of an acre in area.

The graph again shows the large amount of feeding done by Ivory-bills on sweet gum, Nuttall's oak, and hackberry. The graph also shows that Ivory-bills feed mostly upon trees that are over a foot in diameter, even though the majority

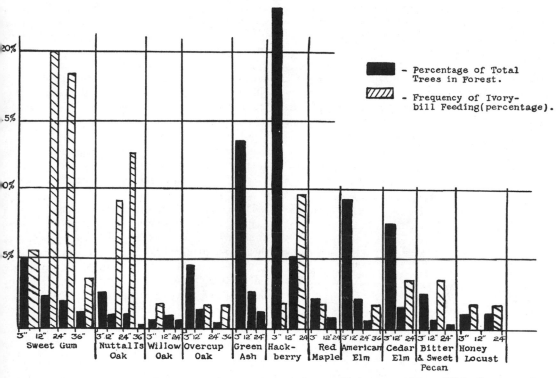

Fig. 20. Comparison of abundance of species and size of trees in forest, with frequency of Ivory-bill feeding on species and size of trees, Singer Tract, La.

of trees in the forest are less than that in size. The following table sums the percentages of size groups present in the forest and the Ivory-bill feeding on each, without regard to species.

Size class, inches	Percent in forest	Percent of Ivory-bill feeding
3–12	75.1	12.7
12–24	18.3	49.0
24–36	5.2	34.7
36 plus	1.4	3.6

The reason for Ivory-bills feeding more frequently on the bigger trees is that large, old trees have more dead and dying wood. Young trees grow rapidly and are resistant to the attacks of insects and disease. As trees 'mature,' their growth slows and becomes less vigorous, decay begins, insects attack them, and woodpeckers come after the insects.

In the Singer Tract I collected borers from several situations similar to places where Ivory-bills fed. The following is a list of the situations and collections:

Sweet gum, under the bark of dead limbs; all larvae:
  Aegomorphus decipiens (Hald.)
  Leptostylus Lec. sp.
  Dendroides sp.
  Urographus fasciata (De. G.)
Nuttall's oak, under bark; all larvae:
  Urographus fasciata (De. G.)
  also larvae of Pyrochoidae, Elateridae-Elaterinae, and Buprestidae-Polycestrinae.
Willow oak, under bark of dead limb; all larvae:
  Leptostylus Lec. sp.
  Urographus fasciata (De. G.)
  Xyoltrechus colonus (Fab.)
Hackberry, dead, in trunk; all larvae:
  Stenodontes dasystomus (Say)
  Parandra brunnea (Fab.)
  Alus oculatus L.
(Generic and specific identifications by F. C. Craighead)

It is very probable that the above-listed kinds of insect larvae are eaten by Ivory-bills, as they were found in situations where Ivory-bills do much of their feeding.

Pileated Woodpeckers are relatively common in the habitat of Ivory-bills and, like the Ivory-bill, their food consists mostly of boring insects and insect larvae, but there are some differences in the feeding habits of the two. The table below shows the results of feeding observations made on the Pileated Woodpecker in the Singer Tract, for comparison with the tabulation of feeding observations on the Ivory-bill.

SUMMARY OF THE FEEDING OBSERVATIONS ON THE PILEATED WOODPECKER IN THE SINGER TRACT, LA., 1937–39

Tree Species	Relative abundance[1]	No. of observations		Percentage of total		Total[2]
		Scl	Dig	Scl	Dig	
Sweet gum	20.8	5	9	10.4	18.7	29.1
Nuttall's oak	10.6	1	4	2.1	8.3	10.4
Willow oak	6.4	0	0	0	0	0
Water oak	3.2	1	2	2.1	4.2	6.3
Overcup oak	8.9	0	4	0	8.3	8.3
Green ash	14.6	1	5	2.1	10.4	12.5
Hackberry	15.4	1	3	2.1	6.3	8.4
Red maple	2.7	0	0	0	0	0
American elm	10.2	1	4	2.1	8.3	10.4
Cedar elm	2.5	1	2	2.1	4.2	6.3
Pecan and water hickory	2.7	0	4	0	8.3	8.3
Honey locust	1.8	0	0	0	0	0
Persimmon	0.2	0	0	0	0	0
Bald cypress	0.2	0	0	0	0	0
	100.2	11	37	23.0	77.0	100.0

Comparison of the two tables shows that the Pileated Woodpecker obtains most of its food by digging for borers in the wood, instead of by scaling. Pileateds did 77% of their feeding by digging, 23% by scaling, which is an almost exact reversal of the feeding habits of the Ivory-bill. What scaling Pileateds were observed to do was mostly on loose bark and was never as extensive or cleanly done as the work of the Ivory-bills. Pileateds also fed more upon sweet gum than upon any other tree, but no more than the relative abundance of that tree in the forest; in fact, the frequency of Pileated feedings in each species was almost in proportion to the abundance of that species—they appeared to have no preference for any species of tree.

The important difference between the feeding habits of the two woodpeckers is that the Ivory-bill feeds mostly on the borers that live beneath the bark of freshly dead wood, while the Pileated feeds mostly on the borers that live within the sap and heart of longer dead wood. The possible significance of this difference in feeding habits is discussed in a following chapter treating of the effect of the quantity of food on the abundance of the Ivory-bill.

The Ivory-bill, like other woodpeckers, is well adapted for its feeding habits of securing borers from beneath the bark and in wood. Its hard chisel-pointed bill is fitted for digging and chiseling; its long extensible tongue is fitted for reaching and spearing borers; and its feet and tail for climbing and clinging in all places. The Ivory-bill, by virtue of its size, is much stronger than other woodpeckers, and is capable of easily scaling away heavy bark that other woodpeckers could not loosen. Even the Pileated is not able to remove hard, tight bark with anything like the speed of the Ivory-bill. Thus, the Ivory-bill is able to reach a supply of food that is not easily accessible to other woodpeckers.

Twice I have observed Ivory-bills drinking. Once the male Ivory-bill drank from a knot-formed hollow that held water on the top of a hackberry limb. The second time, the female bird, just before going to roost, drank from the hollow stub of a broken sweet gum limb. Neither bird took more than a few swallows.

Summary of Food Habits of the Ivory-billed Woodpecker

The Ivory-billed Woodpecker feeds mostly upon wood-boring insect larvae. It secures most of its food by scaling the bark from trees that have recently died, in search of the borers that live between the bark and sapwood, which are largely larval Cerambycids, Buprestids, and Elaterids, three different families of beetles. In the bottomlands of the Mississippi Delta, the Ivory-bill does most of its feeding on sweet gum, Nuttall's oak, and hackberry trees; in Florida it has been observed feeding on pine and cypress. It feeds primarily on the larger trees of the forest, 87% being on trees that are over a foot in diameter, many of its feeding trees being large, old trees subject to decay and insect attacks.

Ivory-bills also feed upon fruits, nuts, seeds, and similar vegetable material on occasion, but these are not as important a food as are insect larvae.

From the standpoint of the kinds of food eaten by the Ivory-bill, its food habits are economically beneficial. More than any other woodpecker it feeds upon the borers that live in freshly dead timber, the borers that live beneath the bark; it is this kind of borer that spreads when very abundant from dead timber to living timber and causes the death of living trees. Sometimes an outbreak of such borers will cause extensive 'worm-kills,' when trees over a large area will be killed by the infestation of these insects.

Woodpeckers, including the Ivory-bill, are probably the chief enemy of such insects and the agent that usually prevents damaging outbreaks. One Ivory-bill can undoubtedly eat more borers than any other woodpecker, but the bird has for many years been too few in numbers to do much actual good.

CHAPTER 9

The Effect of Quantity of Food on the Distribution of the Ivory-billed Woodpecker

IVORY-BILLED Woodpeckers have almost always lived in virgin or primitive stands of timber. Such stands of timber have many old, dying, and dead trees, and these trees, dying or dead, contain boring insects which are the food of woodpeckers. Woodpeckers are much more abundant in virgin timber than where it has been cut over, where the big timber has been removed leaving only the young healthy saplings; the mature timber in uncut stands can supply food for a much larger woodpecker population than can younger timber in cut over or second growth. In northern Louisiana, in the Singer Tract, there were from three to six pairs of Pileated Woodpeckers per square mile of virgin timber, but in the second growth adjacent to the tract there was less than one pair of Pileateds per square mile.

Even in virgin timber Ivory-bills live in the types of timber and in areas where other woodpeckers are commonest. The sweet gum-oak bottomland forest was and is the habitat of the Ivory-bill in the Mississippi Delta, and is also the forest association that supports the greatest number of other woodpeckers; both the cypress-tupelo swamp association and the overcup oak-water hickory association are forest types which Ivory-bills rarely inhabit and which support fewer numbers of all woodpeckers than does the sweet gum-oak association. Thus, it appears that Ivory-bills live in the habitat that furnishes the optimum conditions for woodpeckers.

The Ivory-bill population and ranges in the Singer Tract, Louisiana, have not remained constant, as can be readily seen from the earlier section treating the history of the Ivory-bills in the tract. Some of the changes of Ivory-bill distribution in the tract have coincided with changes in the timber of certain areas. In 1931 a cyclone ripped a swath through the forest near the northeast corner of the tract, felling and killing many trees. Most of the timber was salvaged by a hurried logging operation, but there remained a large amount of freshly killed timber. J. J. Kuhn did not remember seeing Ivory-bills in that area until 1933, about two years after the storm, but he and other natives recalled seeing Ivory-bills around the cyclone area during 1933 and 1934. The birds apparently left that area soon after 1934. In 1930–31, the timber on Sharkey Plantation, a private holding within the Singer Tract, was cut, producing more dead trees and branches. During 1933 and 1934 a pair of Ivory-bills ranged in the tract along the north edge of that cutting, between there and Little Bear Lake.

There has been very little study by entomologists of the insect population of dead trees, and what studies have been made almost disregard the changes in numbers of the insect population. Blackman and Stage's study of the succession of insects living in dead hickory in New York state comes the closest to recording the quantitative changes through the first years of dead trees. They (1924) found that in hickory the greatest number of forms and the greatest number of individuals occurred in the second and third summers after the death of the trees. The few observations and collections I have made in Louisiana indicate about the same, that the numbers of wood-boring insects are most abundant in wood two to three years dead.

Twice in the Singer Tract, as has been described, an unusual amount of timber was killed, and about two years afterward Ivory-bills moved into the vicinity of each deadening and remained there for two or more years. The period of their stay in the areas coincided with the time when wood-boring insects were abundant.

There are other incidents and occurrences indicating that Ivory-bills range and feed in areas where food is most abundant. In the recent history of the birds in the Santee swamp of South Carolina, Ivory-bills were observed in the Wadmacaun Island section, Georgetown County, during 1935 and 1936, years when mast was abundant in that part of the swamp, but no sign of them could be found there in the succeeding years when mast was scarce.

During the latter months of 1937, Oscar E.

Baynard frequently saw Ivory-bills near Highlands Hammock State Park, Highlands County, Florida. He saw them in a small swamp near the park where many cypress trees had been killed, apparently by fire, and the woodpeckers were feeding in the deadening. Ivory-bills were not seen near the park after the end of 1937; when I visited the area about a year later, the bark had fallen from the dead cypress, the sapwood was rotten, and few woodpeckers were there.

In the late summer of 1928 a storm killed some pine timber at Wakulla Beach, Wakulla County, Florida, and Mrs. Hall of that locality several times saw an Ivory-bill feeding in that storm-killed timber (H. L. Stoddard, epist.). Herbert L. Stoddard visited that place in January 1929 and, although he saw no Ivory-bills, he examined several pine trees that had been stripped of bark by a strong woodpecker, in a manner in which he had seen Ivory-bills feed during his youth in central Florida. A. T. Wayne (1893) stated that in the Suwannee region of Florida Ivory-bills were best found around 'burn-outs,' tracts of heavy timber which fire had destroyed and which harbored beetles and borers.

In parts of the Singer Tract, Louisiana, in the Santee in South Carolina, and near Highlands Hammock State Park, Florida, Ivory-bills have ranged in areas where there appeared to be an abundant supply of food for them, and they disappeared from those areas when the amount of woodpecker food diminished. Other instances have been described when Ivory-bills were found in places where there was an unusually, even abnormally, large supply of food for woodpeckers, such as occurs in storm or fire-killed timber. These occurrences suggested that some unexplained changes in the population and ranges of Ivory-bills in the Singer Tract might have been caused by unobserved changes in the food supply, and studies were made there in an attempt to correlate the amount of available woodpecker food with Ivory-bill numbers and ranges.

Histories of Ivory-bills in the John's Bayou, Mack's Bayou, and Greenlea Bend areas were known best, so in 1938 those three areas were chosen for examination. Counts were made of the frequency and ages of dead wood present, since that roughly determines the amount of woodpecker food available. The method used was to count all trees, all trees bearing dead wood, and all standing dead trees and trunks in a circle of sixty-feet radius, this giving a plot approximately a quarter of an acre in area. The plots were chosen at random by walking one hundred yards from the center of the last plot counted, the end of the one hundred yards being the center of the next plot. Usually four plots were counted in this manner, thus covering a total of one acre in four plots separated over three hundred yards, in all parts of each of the areas.

Each tree was tallied as to species and whether it had wood that had been dead less than two years, or dead wood two to four years old, or dead wood more than four years old. The age of the dead wood was estimated by such signs as the presence or absence of twigs and small branches, the tightness and hardness of the bark, and the condition of the wood. (Trees and limbs two years dead have lost almost all twigs, some small branches, and bark is loosened on small branches; trees and limbs four years dead have lost all small branches, many large ones, and small trees have lost larger limbs.)

The following table shows the frequency of dead wood in each of the three areas. In making counts, the species of trees were recorded, but there seemed to be no significant differences between the species so they are lumped together.

FREQUENCY OF TREES WITH DEAD WOOD, SINGER TRACT LA.

Average number of trees per acre with dead wood of each age class. (Standard deviation of count in parenthesis.)

Area	4 plus	Years Dead 2–4	0–2
John's Bayou	3.1 (2.80)	3.4 (1.42)	7.5 (3.34)
Mack's Bayou	4.6 (1.52)	2.4 (1.52)	4.8 (3.13)
Greenlea Bend	3.5 (2.53)	3.5 (1.38)	5.5 (2.75)
Mean of the three areas	3.7	3.1	5.9

	Number of acres examined	Average number of all trees per acre
John's Bayou	10	195.6 (44.3)
Mack's Bayou	5	161.2 (21.0)
Greenlea Bend	6	113.7 (27.8)

Counts for the three areas were tested for statistical significance, using the t-test and the method for comparing groups of different sizes (G. W. Snedecor). The following table shows the probability, expressed as a percentage, that the areas compared are alike or homogeneous.

PERCENTAGE OF PROBABILITY THAT THE AREAS COMPARED ARE ALIKE OR HOMOGENEOUS

	Age Class			
Comparison of:	4 plus	2–4	0–2	All trees per acre
John's Bayou and Mack's Bayou areas	18%	1–%	16%	12%
John's Bayou and Greenlea Bend areas	75%	19%	21%	1–%
Mack's Bayou and Greenlea Bend areas	42%	1–%	65%	1–%

A probability of 5%, or a chance of only one out of twenty, is generally considered to indicate a significant difference; a probability of less than 5% is an even better indication of a true or significant difference.

The only groups that differ significantly from others of the same class are the number of trees in the Mack's Bayou area with dead wood two to four years old, and the total number of trees per acre in the Greenlea Bend area; in each case there is less than one percent probability that these groups are homogeneous with the other areas, or, in other words, the chances are more than 100 to 1 that these groups are different. Thus, the Mack's Bayou area differs significantly from the other two areas in the number of trees per acre with dead wood two to four years old, and the Greenlea Bend area differs from the others in the average number of all trees per acre.

There was quite a difference between some of the areas in the average number of trees per acre with dead wood of a certain age; for instance, John's Bayou had an average of 7.5 trees per acre with dead wood less than two years old, as compared with Mack's Bayou area which had an average of 4.8 trees per acre with dead wood of that age. But the counts within each area were so variable that the differences between the averages were not significant except in the cases described in the preceding paragraph. In some of the groups compared the probability that they were homogeneous was about 16% to 21% (see table), and while these percentages are not low enough to be truly significant, they at least indicate that there might have been significant differences between the areas. If more plots in each area had been counted, thus increasing the number of counts, there is a good possibility that significant differences might have been obtained between some of these groups. Unfortunately, I was not able to evaluate my counts before I left the Singer Tract, and so did not realize the need of making more counts while I was there. Despite the lack of statistical proof that all the differences between the averages are significant, there are indications that this is so in several groups, and evidence will be presented later to show that the averages for the areas are a good measure of the relative frequency of trees with dead wood.

My objective in computing the frequency of dead wood in these three areas in the forest was to compare the three areas as to the abundance of wood recently or long dead in each, and to judge if there had been any change in the rate of tree death in the last few years in each area.

The different age classes cannot accurately be compared with each other, because many of the branches that had died more than two years before had dropped from the tree and so were lost. That explains why there were about twice as many trees counted with wood less than two years dead, and why so comparatively few trees bore wood more than four years dead.

The three areas can be compared, however, by comparing the number of trees with dead wood of each age with the mean of all three areas for that age (see table). For the John's Bayou area the number of trees in the '4 plus' age class is less than the mean for the three areas, in the '2–4' age class it is slightly greater, and in the last and most recent age class it is considerably greater than the mean. On the other hand, for the Mack's Bayou area the number starts above and then falls below the mean in going from the older to the recent age class. The numbers for the Greenlea Bend area fluctuate around the mean of the three areas.

Another way to state this is to say that in the John's Bayou area the rate of tree death rose

Plate 11.   Dead trunk of a hackberry, fed upon frequently by Ivory-bills.

Plate 12.   A dying sweet gum tree on which Ivory-bills have fed many times.

Plate 13.   Male Ivory-bill at nest.   Singer Tract, La., April 1935.

Plate 14. Roost hole in a dead green ash, used regularly by a male Ivory-bill.

above the average for the three areas, in the Mack's Bayou area it started above and then fell below the average, and in the Greenlea Bend area it fluctuated around the average.

It must be remembered that all of the group counts on which this comparison is based are not significantly different from each other, but the low probability percentages for some of the group comparisons indicate at least that there might have been significant differences between the areas, and this indication is supported by other facts. In 1924 a bad fire burned over much of the Singer Tract, and in the Mack's Bayou area many trees were damaged so severely as eventually to die. The timber wardens of the Singer Tract said that many trees died and fell in that area; that is shown by the frequent breaks in the forest canopy of that part of the forest, where trees have fallen so long ago that most of them have disappeared, but so recently that younger trees have not had time to fill the breaks. The rate of tree death in that area was high several years ago, but it has decreased within the last few years probably because the trees injured by the fire have disappeared and the remaining trees are comparatively healthy.

John's Bayou area was also burned over by the same fire, but the damage done to the timber was not so severe, and there was no such loss of trees in that area as there was around Mack's Bayou. Many trees in the John's Bayou area show fire scars at the base of the trunk, places unprotected by bark where fungus and insect enemies can attack, which were not severe enough to lead to the death of the tree but could lead to their weakening. Greenlea Bend was not burned over by the 1924 fire and so the timber there was unaffected.

If the comparative rate of tree death in the three areas is as has been related in a preceding paragraph, the woodpecker population should be highest in the areas described as having the highest rate of tree death, since woodpeckers are almost dependent on dead or dying wood to supply food. The John's Bayou area has the highest rate of tree death measured, and the average estimate (in the breeding season) of the numbers of woodpeckers present in that area was twelve Pileated and sixty-four Red-bellied Woodpeckers

per square mile. Mack's Bayou area, with a decreasing rate of tree death measured, was estimated to have an average of slightly under nine Pileated and about forty Red-bellied Woodpeckers per square mile; Greenlea Bend with the measured rate of tree death fluctuating around the mean of the three areas, had an average of slightly over eight Pileated and about forty Red-bellied Woodpeckers per square mile. The abundance of woodpeckers in the three areas roughly reflects the measured abundance of trees with dead wood and the measured rate of tree death in each area.

Thus, the average number of trees per acre with dead wood of each age has been confirmed as a good measure of the relative rate of tree death in the three areas, partly by statistical significance of the counts, partly by known history of the areas, of fires and the effect of fires on the timber, and partly by the relative abundance of Pileated and Red-bellied Woodpeckers in the different areas.

The final objective in making these counts and comparisons was to see if there was any relation between the abundance of dead wood or the rate of tree death in each area and the history of the Ivory-bills in the area. In John's Bayou area the rate of tree death apparently rose above the average, and the Ivory-bills have nested in that area for the past few years, one pair of Ivory-bills nesting there since at least 1935. In the Mack's Bayou area, the rate of tree death fell below the average in the last few years, and the number of Ivory-bills there has decreased; the last year that a pair was known to nest in that area was 1935. In Greenlea Bend, where the rate of tree death varied around the average, the number of Ivory-bills has also decreased, and since 1937 has apparently consisted of one bird. The only part of the tract where the numbers of breeding Ivory-bills have not decreased in the last few years is the area which had the greatest amount of recently dead timber and the highest rate of tree death, the John's Bayou area. This was also the area with the greatest number of Pileated and Red-bellied Woodpeckers.

The rate of tree death in the John's Bayou area rose above the average, but that does not mean that the rate of tree death in that area actually increased, for the average rate of tree death in the three areas and probably over the entire tract decreased within the last few years. Since the fire of 1924 in the Singer Tract there has been nothing to cause an increase in the rate of timber deterioration or tree death, and the condition of the timber in the tract probably improved as the effects of the fire disappeared through the death and disappearance of the fire-injured trees. It is also the opinion of some of the men connected with the Singer Tract that the rate of timber depreciation has decreased. Since the average rate of tree death most probably decreased, the rate of tree death in the John's Bayou area probably remained about constant and the actual rate of tree death in the other areas declined more or less sharply.

To summarize this comparison of the rate of tree death and the history of the Ivory-bills in three areas of the Singer Tract: the average number of trees per acre with dead wood of different ages for each of the three areas was obtained. There were significant differences between some of the averages; between others the differences were not significant but were indicated, the probability of which was supported by other evidence. The John's Bayou area apparently had the greatest amount of recently dead timber and the highest rate of tree death during the past few years, and the breeding Ivory-bill population remained constant during that time. In the Mack's Bayou and Greenlea Bend areas the rates of tree death were less than in the John's Bayou area, and the numbers of Ivory-bills in both of these areas decreased. The comparative abundance of woodpecker food in the John's Bayou area was also indicated by that area having the greatest density of Pileated and Red-bellied Woodpeckers. Numbers of Ivory-bills in these three areas of the Singer Tract were apparently directly correlated with the quantity of dead or dying wood, which determines the abundance of woodpecker food; changes in the quantity of their food apparently caused changes in the numbers and distribution of the Ivory-bills. During recent years there evidently has been a decrease in the rate of tree death and timber deterioration over the entire Singer Tract, as fire-injured trees died and disappeared;

this could only result in fewer numbers of woodpeckers, including the Ivory-bill, and is most probably the cause or at least one cause for the decrease of Ivory-bills in the tract.

According to A. Carlson (epist.) of Trumann, Arkansas, an official supervising the Singer Tract, the amount of sweet gum timber in the tract decreased 40% between 1911 and 1923, when timber estimates were made in the tract; in twelve years over 300 million board feet of timber died probably due in part to a fire in 1917. If this estimate of the deterioration is accurate, there must have been a tremendous number of dead and dying trees during that period, and conditions must have been excellent for large numbers of woodpeckers. Ivory-bills may well have been more numerous then than during any other time in the history of the tract. Some of the older natives of the region have said that Ivory-bills were once more common in the tract than during recent years, and if that is true, the high rate of timber deterioration and death between 1911 and 1923 was probably the cause.

In May of 1939 I attempted to make an estimate of the kinds of wood-boring insects present in the woods of the Singer Tract, and the relative amounts of each kind, chiefly to see if there was any difference in the relative abundance of wood-boring insects between the situations where the Ivory-bills usually feed and where Pileated Woodpeckers usually feed. Wood-boring insects were collected in the fresh cut-over northwest of Horseshoe Lake, where most of the trees had been felled to the ground and the dead parts were accessible. Eight quarter-acre plots, totaling two acres, were examined closely, and insects collected from all samples of dead wood found in the plots. A fraction of the log, or piece of dead wood was taken and examined thoroughly for all the insects in it, and the insects or larvae were preserved. Recorded for each collection were the species and description of the dead wood and the size of the fraction that was examined. Later, in the laboratory, the insects collected were identified at least to family, and the volume of each sample was measured by displacement. The total volume of insects in the dead wood for the entire two acres was calculated by knowing the volume of the insects collected and the fraction of dead wood from which the collections were made. The following table presents a summary of the results and estimates of the collecting.

TABULATION OF THE KINDS AND AMOUNTS OF DEAD WOOD AND WOOD-BORING INSECTS IN TWO ACRES, SINGER TRACT, LA.

Description	Total of situation in 2 acres	Families and numbers of insects collected	Estimated total vol. insects per 2 acres
Under bark of dead limbs; situations where Ivory-bills feed	80 sq. ft.	Carabidae 1 ad Cerambycidae 1 ad Buprestidae 1 lv Elateridae 11 lv Pyrochoidae 8 lv	27 cc.
In stump, hard but partly punky; situation where both Ivory-bills and Pileateds feed	30 cu. ft.	Cerambycidae 9 lv	237 cc.
In dead limbs, punky, and punky and rotten tree trunks and logs; situations where Pileateds feed	386 cu. ft.	Buprestidae 4 lv Cerambycidae 7 lv Elateridae 3 lv Lucanidae 1 lv Passalidae 11 ad Passalidae 14 lv Tenebrionidae 8 lv unidentified 2 pupae	1154 cc.

(abbreviations: ad = adult; lv = larvae)

In the two acres a volume of 27 cc. insects was found under the dead bark where Ivory-bills feed, 237 cc. in places where both Ivory-bills and Pileateds feed, and 1154 cc. in punky and rotten wood where Pileateds usually feed and Ivory-bills do not. The volume of food used solely by the Pileated was about forty times that fed upon by the Ivory-bill alone.

In the two areas examined there was an unusually low number of branches and limbs that had been dead only a year or two, the kind that Ivory-bills habitually feed upon. I was able to find but two samples of dead wood of this kind in the two acres where in the three areas that were examined for frequency of dead wood there was an average of at least five trees with recently dead wood in one acre. An examination of this area before the timber was cut probably would have revealed at least a few dead limbs and branches in the tree tops, but when the trees were felled, the tops were so smashed on hitting the ground that it was almost impossible to find in the jumbled heap of broken limbs and branches wood that had been dead on the tree.

Because so comparatively little recently dead wood was found in the two acres, the amount of Ivory-bill food discovered was undoubtedly less than was actually there, and the calculated proportion of Pileated to Ivory-bill food was quite a bit greater than normal. It would be impossible to estimate accurately from the data at hand the probable proportion, for the entire tract, of insects that live in long dead wood, where Pileateds usually feed, to insects that live under the bark, where Ivory-bills usually feed, i.e., of Pileated food to Ivory-bill food; but there is apparently a much greater number and volume of the former kind of wood-boring insects.

The reason for this is simple. When a tree dies, insects living beneath the bark attack it first, reach their peak of abundance about two years after the death of the tree, and then decrease and disappear. Insects that bore within the wood follow, and this type inhabits the gradually decaying and rotting wood until the tree has almost completely rotted away, which may be ten years or more after the tree's death. Therefore, in any area, there is likely to be a much greater number of insects that live deep in rotten wood, for dead wood is habitable to those kinds of wood-borers for several more years than it is to borers that live beneath the bark.

Ivory-bills can find the kind of food they seem to prefer in a dead tree or limb for but a short period after its death, but Pileateds feed upon a tree until it has almost returned to earth. In an ordinary forest there is much more food available to the manner of feeding of a Pileated than to that of an Ivory-bill. Very likely the proportion of Pileated to Ivory-bill food is not as great as was found in the area examined, but it is probably the chief reason for the greater number of Pileateds. The relative abundance of Pileated and Ivory-billed Woodpeckers, estimated from their probable maximum density, was thirty-six Pileateds to one Ivory-bill. This is greater than the probable proportion of Pileated food to Ivory-bill food, so the relative quantity of food is not the only factor deciding the relative abundance of the two species. Other influencing factors are the larger size of the Ivory-bill and the increased difficulty of finding the food which is less abundant and less evenly distributed.

I do not know why Ivory-bills should prefer to feed upon insect borers that are relatively scarce, unless it be that when the borers beneath the bark are abundant, they are very abundant. Probably the total number of borers in a dead tree is greatest for the short period when the borers beneath the bark are at the peak of their abundance. The number of such borers is much more likely to be variable, from place to place and from time to time, than is the number of insects boring in long dead wood. The Ivory-bill's insect food supply is smaller, more variable or erratic, and more unevenly distributed than that of the Pileated.

Summary of the Effect of Quantity of Food on the Numbers of Ivory-billed Woodpeckers

Ivory-billed Woodpeckers inhabit forests where woodpecker food and other woodpeckers are most abundant. In the Mississippi Delta and other bottomland forests, the sweet gum-oak association is the type of forest that supports the largest population of woodpeckers and it is likewise the preferred habitat of the Ivory-bill.

Instances have occurred where timber has been killed by storm, fire, or logging operations, and the Ivory-bills have lived in the vicinity of these deadenings only during the period when boring insects, especially those that live beneath the bark, were most abundant. A survey was made in the Singer Tract, Louisiana, in the three areas where the history of the Ivory-bill was best known, to measure the frequency or abundance of dead wood and the changes in the rate of tree death in each area. In the John's Bayou area, dead wood, especially wood dead less than two years, was most abundant, the rate of tree death had risen above the average, and Pileated and Red-bellied Woodpeckers were most abundant. The number of breeding Ivory-bills in this area has remained constant in recent years. In the other two areas recently dead wood was less abundant than formerly, the rate of tree death had decreased with or below the average, and the number of Ivory-bills had decreased.

Ivory-bills have ranged in areas where there was an unusually large amount of recently dead wood due to some catastrophe to the timber, such as storm or fire, and have left these areas as the dead timber aged; and Ivory-bills have decreased in number in areas where the rate of tree death has declined and the quantity of their food decreased. Decline in the numbers of Ivory-bills in the Singer Tract within recent years was probably caused by a decrease in the amount of timber death over the entire tract.

The proportion between the quantity of insects in long dead wood, where Pileateds feed, and the quantity in recently dead wood, where Ivory-bills feed, was estimated in a two-acre area and there found to be forty to one; there was forty times as much Pileated food found as there was food available for Ivory-bills. This proportion was undoubtedly higher than normal, because the amount of recently dead wood found in the area examined was unusually small. The quantity of food available to Pileateds, however, is always considerably greater than the quantity available to Ivory-bills, and this is probably the chief reason for the greater numbers of Pileateds. The kind of borers fed upon by Ivory-bills are not only fewer, but are likely to fluctuate in numbers within an area, as they are present in dead timber a comparatively short period during the process of decay.

The Ivory-bill appears to be a woodpecker dependent upon an abundant food supply, in quantity greater than is usually present in the average forest. Wood-boring insects are plentiful only when there is a large number of dying or dead trees, such as is caused by fire or storms, or perhaps when a large number of trees happen to weaken and die at the same time from old age. Such deaths of timber causing outbreaks of borers occur irregularly and are likely to be widely scattered, since they are in the nature of accidents. The Ivory-bill must be a wide-ranging species if it depends for existence on such unusual numbers of borers, and evidence that has been presented indicates that they are wide-ranging birds (chapter on 'Population, Density and Individual Range'), strong fliers, traveling usually in pairs, feeding in areas where woodpecker food is plentiful and capable of moving to other suitable areas when food becomes scarce.

One of the most frequent causes for the death of large quantities of timber is fire, and in Florida and the southeastern states much Ivory-bill feeding was done in fire-killed timber. The question arises as to whether woods fires occurred in the Southeast before the coming of the white man. They almost undoubtedly occurred as far back as man of any race lived in this country, and fires probably occurred even before then. The long-leaf pine requires fire for successful seeding and regeneration, and its evolution therefore must have been shaped by fire, and fire must have affected the southern forests for a very long time. Fire probably was the most important agent of timber death, and Ivory-bills living in mixed swamp and pine forest in the southeastern states probably secured a large proportion of their food in fire-killed timber.

Cutting the forests of the South has removed the large old trees which produce Ivory-bill food, and has reduced the chances of storm and fire-killed timber occurring and producing still greater quantities of borers. This has likewise prevented Ivory-bills from ranging widely by making large areas extremely unsuited to them. The Ivory-bill is adapted to living in large forests, where it can find areas with an abundant supply of the type of borers it feeds upon; the destruction or isolation of such forests has made it increasingly difficult for the bird to find sufficient food and to move from one area to another in search of a variable food supply that has always been more or less eruptive and undependable.

CHAPTER 10

Other Factors Affecting the Ivory-billed Woodpecker

Competitors

THE Ivory-billed Woodpecker has no real competitors for its food supply. It is the only woodpecker which feeds mostly on the borers that live beneath the bark of recently dead trees and its size and strength enable it to loosen hard and tight bark to secure insects there that smaller woodpeckers cannot obtain. Ivory-bills also live in woods where other woodpeckers are most abundant, are absent where others are scarce, and so are apparently not at all affected by the numbers of other woodpeckers.

Ivory-bills and Pileateds rarely seem to notice each other. On April 23, 1939, I watched four Ivory-bills and two Pileateds feed together in the same tree for almost a half hour without paying any obvious attention to each other, and once J. J. Kuhn saw a Pileated quietly pass an Ivory-bill on the opposite side of a medium-sized tree. Only once did I see any apparent antagonism between the species, when a year-old male Ivory-bill several times chased a pair of Pileateds. He flew at the Pileateds when they were pecking on limbs, scared them away, and then pecked for himself in the same place for a few moments; this behavior resembled more the action I have seen of young birds following their parents and pushing them away to peck in the workings of the adults than it did any deliberate driving away of the Pileateds. The Ivory-bill chased one pair of Pileateds several times and a little later did the same to a third. They all gave way to the bigger bird silently, moved a short way off, and called and scolded.

Predators

There are no records or known observations of Ivory-bills being attacked by predators of any kind, nor any evidence of that happening. Yet predators affect the actions of Ivory-bills at least during the nesting season and when the young are just out of the nest.

On April 2, 1939, when the young Ivory-bill was still in the nest, a large Cooper's Hawk perched about thirty yards from the nest. The adult Ivory-bills immediately flew toward it, the male giving an almost continual cackling scold; both woodpeckers perched near the hawk, scolding. When the hawk flew, they chased it until it had left the vicinity of the nest, when they returned to a tree near the nest for a few minutes before flying off. On March 9, 1938, the female Ivory-bill scolded and chased away a Red-shouldered Hawk that flew over and perched near the nest. The young bird was out of the nest and feeding with the parents on June 8, 1937, when a Pileated Woodpecker started calling slowly. The female Ivory-bill gave one short yap, flew to the tree where the young was perched, then to another nearby tree where she remained silent. A few minutes later a Red-shouldered Hawk flew from an adjacent tree. A few times I have seen Ivory-bills call suddenly and then sidle around to the under side of the limb as they watched a hawk or vulture pass over.

Resident hawks that might affect Ivory-bills are the Red-shouldered, Red-tailed, and Cooper's Hawks. The commonest is the Red-shouldered, and that is hardly large and strong enough to attack an Ivory-bill. There are records of Red-tailed and Cooper's Hawks attacking birds the size of an Ivory-bill, but they are unusual, and judging from the actions of the Ivory-bills toward a Cooper's, described above, the birds are not particularly afraid of one. The Duck Hawk is a regular migrant and a very rare breeding bird in the Ivory-bill range. It occasionally kills Pileated Woodpeckers. It is, however, comparatively rare, and since it usually hunts in the open, especially near lakes and waterways it is very unlikely that one would ever have the opportunity to stoop at an Ivory-bill. The Cooper's and Red-tail, that hunt in the woods, are more apt to attack an Ivory-bill. The Ivory-bill's size, its alertness, and its aggressiveness in driving hawks away from the vicinity of young or nests seem to be adequate protection from these birds.

The Barred Owl is the only large, common owl

in the Ivory-bill range. The size of adult Ivory-bills and their habit of roosting in holes probably protect them from attacks by owls. It apparently takes some time for a young Ivory-bill just out of the nest to learn to roost in holes. The times that I have watched the young bird leave the nest, it roosted the first night clinging to a large vertical limb in a rather exposed position. Three days after leaving the nest the young bird roosted in a leafy-topped tree where it was well hidden. I do not know how long it is before the young start roosting in holes, but for the first few nights at least they roost in a rather exposed position where they might be attacked by owls.

The Ivory-bill's habit of feeding and living almost its whole life in and near the tops of trees makes it very unlikely that any mammal could prey on one. Only rarely does an Ivory-bill come close enough to the ground to be within reach of a bob-cat or other four-legged predator.

Shooting and Collecting of the Ivory-billed Wood-pecker

The Ivory-billed Woodpecker was sought after by man even before white men became established on this continent. Mark Catesby in 1731 wrote: "The bills of these birds are much valued by the 'Canadian Indians' who make coronets of 'em for their princes and great warriors. . . The 'Northern Indians'. . . purchase them from the 'Southern' people at the price of two, and sometimes three buckskins a bill." So even at that early time the rarity of Ivory-bills and the difficulty of securing them had created a considerable price for them or for the bill, which was an article of trade among Indians. The bill of an Ivory-bill and one of a Pileated Woodpecker were excavated from an Indian grave near Johnstown, Weld County, Colorado, in January of 1939 (A. M. Bailey); that bill must have traveled several hundred miles by trade from the point where the bird was killed.

The bills and sometimes the crests were used in several ways by the Indians. Catesby's description of their use in making coronets has already been cited. Audubon (1831) wrote that the entire belts of Indian chiefs were closely ornamented with the tufts and bills of Ivory-billed Woodpeckers.

A peace pipe in the Public Museum of Milwaukee, from the Iowa Indians of Oklahoma, is ornamented with six bills and crests of the Ivory-bill (Crabb, 1930).

There are varied interpretations of the use by Indians of the bills and crests of the Ivory-bill. A. M. Bailey (1939) states that parts of woodpeckers were supposed to be specific cures for venereal diseases. E. D. Crabb (1930), quoting Harrington, writes that "the dried head of an Ivory-bill woodpecker within the sacred bundle is supposed to give the man the woodpecker's power of seeking out and capturing his prey" and of cutting a big hole in the enemy. Whatever the significance, the size, rarity and almost spectacular appearance of the Ivory-bill no doubt gave its bill added powers.

The coming of the white man and his propensity for making collections of things increased the killing of the Ivory-bill; his gun made it easier. The rarity of the bird and the difficulty of securing one even with a gun gave the Ivory-bill increased value in collections. To quote an anonymous author (1879) writing of the Ivory-bill: "This bird is not at all abundant, and specimens may be regarded as good additions to one's cabinet." The desire of collectors for specimens stimulated both taxidermists and hunters; one man (W. A. D.) killed for collectors between twenty and twenty-five Ivory-bills in ten years near Sanford, Florida.

Taxidermists and collectors who secured Ivory-bills usually paid local hunters a comparatively small price for fresh specimens. Natives of the Suwannee River region remember receiving four or five dollars for each, probably from A. T. Wayne who was the most active taxidermist and collector in that region in 1892 and 1893. Philip Laurent (1917) in the Gulf Hammock, Florida, paid five dollars for a male and two and a half for a female in 1887. W. E. D. Scott (1904), who did much collecting in west central Florida around 1880, stated that he offered a stipulated price for Ivory-bills; at first he obtained some specimens, but that ceasing, he found that the people considered him to be asking an unfair price, for they believed that he took the birds north and sold the ivory for some fabulous price.

The collecting of Ivory-bills undoubtedly greatly reduced or extirpated the birds of certain localities. This almost certainly happened in the lower Suwannee swamp and California swamp, Dixie County, Florida, when A. T. Wayne collected there in 1892 and 1893. Natives there say that Ivory-bills were very rare or non-existent in that area after Wayne's activities. It is impossible to say how many birds have been killed through collecting. In the collections of this country there are now probably between 200 and 250 specimens of Ivory-bills, an estimate based on the number of specimens listed in museum catalogues, in museum collections I examined, etc. Many specimens have probably been collected and lost, either before or after skins were prepared.

Ivory-bills were also killed to secure their bills and heads for curiosities. Audubon (1831) stated that at the "wooding places" of steamboats strangers paid twenty-five cents for two or three heads of the Ivory-bill. Natives of Gulf Hammock and the Suwannee River region of Florida told me that they used to sell the bills of Ivory-bills for as much as five dollars a piece. The ivory appearance of the bill and the name 'Ivory-bill' made many believe that the bill was of genuine, valuable ivory, as in Scott's experience, thus making it seem reasonable to them that the bill had some real value. Bills bought as curiosities were sometimes made into watch charms or fobs.

Legal protection for the Ivory-bill in Florida, where most of the collecting was done, came when the state passed a law in 1901 protecting non-game birds. In 1905 a commercial collector was arrested for shipping Ivory-bill skins from Florida (Dutcher, 1905), and was successfully prosecuted. When the Ivory-bill was 'rediscovered' in Louisiana in 1932, the state conservation department stated that no permits would be issued for the collecting of Ivory-bills, even for scientific purposes (Pearson, 1932).

In one locality at least, Ivory-bills were shot for food; A. T. Wayne (1895) stated that in the Wacissa River region Ivory-bills were considered "better than ducks." I found no other instance of this occurring. In some localities of the South, woodpeckers are shot by fishermen and the meat used to bait the hooks of set or trot lines, and trappers occasionally use woodpecker meat for baiting traps. The much commoner Pileated Woodpecker is the one usually shot for such purposes, but it is possible that an Ivory-bill might occasionally have been killed.

From my experience, the most likely cause for Ivory-bills being shot today is from the curiosity of hunters. Natives of Louisiana in the vicinity of the Singer Tract have told me that they have heard of other persons killing Ivory-bills to see what they looked like, and one man said that he had intended to kill one himself but had never had a chance. The idea of conserving the bird because it is scarce never occurs to them at all. They are only curious and wish to look over a specimen in the hand. It is impossible to judge from the reports how many birds have actually been killed for this reason, for the reports that reached me were all second-hand; at least the teller made it sound second-hand; and some of the birds reported shot were probably Pileateds. A few years ago an extravagant statement was unwisely made in a local paper in northern Louisiana that specimens of Ivory-bills were worth one thousand dollars a piece. At least one bird was killed because of this by a youth hoping to get rich quickly. The statement was not taken at face value by most of the natives because it seemed preposterous, but it did arouse a desire in some to get a close look at this seemingly wonderful bird. Protection of the Singer Tract by state wardens has done much to protect the Ivory-bill, but has not been successful in keeping out all hunters. And the barring of *all* hunters from an Ivory-bill area is the only sure way to keep the birds from being shot.

The collecting and shooting of Ivory-bills has not been the major cause of the species' decrease, has not been as important as the destruction of the Ivory-bill's habitat by logging. But now that there are so few Ivory-bills living, the shooting of a few birds might become the final cause for their extinction. Any species reduced in numbers by one cause might be wiped out by a totally different agent, even in the nature of an accident, killing the last breeding individuals, and this could easily happen to the Ivory-bills. Rigid protection from man will be necessary for the continued existence of the Ivory-billed Woodpecker.

CHAPTER 11

General Habits and Behavior

Daily Routine and Actions, Non-nesting Season

IVORY-BILLED Woodpeckers in the Singer Tract, Louisiana, have fairly definite patterns for their daily activities, that of the nesting season differing from that during the rest of the year. Their activities during the nesting season will be described in the chapter on nesting habits, while the following is a description of their routine during the remainder of the year. Almost all sustained observations of the birds were made on the pair inhabiting the John's Bayou section of the Singer Tract.

The Ivory-bill was almost the last bird of those woods to arise in the morning. Smaller birds started singing at or before daylight during the springtime, and the Pileated and other woodpeckers would be heard soon after daylight, but the earliest that the Ivory-bills appeared from their roost holes was a quarter of an hour after good daylight, and sometimes the sun had lighted the treetops before the birds emerged. The time that the Ivory-bills first appeared was variable; they usually bestirred themselves much later on cloudy mornings. In early March they arose around 6:30 A.M., in May and June from 4:45 to 5:15, and in December from 6.45 to 7:15. The bird usually came out of its roost hole silently, and climbed to the top of the tree where it would often sit, preen, stretch, and peck with some vigor at the limb on which it was perched. After a minute or so it would call once, then more, single *kents;* frequently its mate would answer and then one bird would fly to and join the other. If there were young of the year present, all birds would get together soon after leaving their roost holes. The amount of calling and the place they joined each other varied greatly. Sometimes they would gather on the long-stubbed tree wherein the male bird usually roosted, sometimes in a big tree near the female's roost hole, or again where the young bird roosted. Once together, the birds would start off for feeding. Frequently they preceded their flights by a chorus of loud calls, *kient–kient– kient,* all the birds calling together, and then one would lead off and the others would follow. No particular bird appeared to be the leader. Their flights in the early morning were usually rather long, up to a quarter of a mile, with few and short stops for feeding. It taxed a man's legs and wind to keep up with them. After they had traveled about half a mile, often more or less, they would take more time for feeding and would fly less.

The Ivory-bills usually fed actively, and called frequently until about 10 A.M.; then they would become quiet, almost cease feeding, and do little but sit during the middle of the day. This midday quiescence is more pronounced during the long, hot days of summer than at other seasons. Around 3:30 P.M. they usually became active again, working gradually in the direction of the roosting ground and feeding as they went. They often reached the roosting ground about sunset or before, then dallied in the vicinity, feeding and pecking some, until dusk, when they would separate and quietly go to roost in their holes.

Rainy weather slowed the activities of the Ivory-bills. Indeed, on one morning when rain was falling hard and steadily, the birds did not appear at all even though I stayed near the roost holes until an hour past sunrise. Rain and cold during the middle of the day likewise caused the birds to slow their feeding and often to stop entirely and to cling in some sheltered place on a tree.

Ivory-bills perch like other woodpeckers, usually lengthwise on a limb or tree trunk. Occasionally they will sit across a limb, but that only when they are getting ready to fly. Clinging to a limb or the side of a tree, they grasp the bark with both feet wide apart and forward, and brace with the long springy tail against the side of the tree (Plate 13). Climbing, the bird springs upward, shifting his foothold near the conclusion of each leap. They can climb quite rapidly and apparently without effort, and have no difficulty climbing around the top, side, or underside of a limb.

The actions of Ivory-bills are quick and vigorous, almost nervous. When perched and alert, they have a habit of swinging the body quickly from one side to the other, pivoting on the tail pressed to the tree, pausing to peer back over the shoulder, then swinging back and looking over the other shoulder, at each quick swing flirting the wings. When feeding by knocking off the bark, they hit sidewise blows from both directions, and often pry and knock off the pieces of bark with a flick of the bill. Their method for digging into the wood for borers is like that of the Pileated, chiseling out chips of wood with rapid powerful blows.

Ivory-bills often preen and scratch themselves, especially during the times of the day when they are not actively feeding. They use the bill for most parts of the plumage, and scratch the head and neck with a foot.

The flight of the Ivory-bill has already been partly described in the chapter treating of field identification. It is strong and usually direct, with steady wing-beats. They can take flight quickly either from a perch or from a hole, springing into the air with very little descent before getting up speed. They often fly above the tree tops, dodging the trees with very little deviation from their course. In the thick woods it is ordinarily difficult to tell how far the Ivory-bills fly, but I am quite sure that their flight is often extended for half a mile or more. I have seen the birds fly, have followed in the direction they went, and walked rapidly for half a mile or more before finding them again, enjoying their leisure in a tree top. They end their flights with a quick upward swoop and a few braking wing-beats, usually landing on a vertical tree trunk or slightly inclined limb. In most short flights, from limb to limb or one tree to an adjacent one, they beat the wings, unless the flight is downward when they are likely to glide and swoop.

Audubon (1831) describes the longer flights of Ivory-bills as undulating, like Pileateds', but I observed this only once when a year-old male Ivory-bill flew a short distance with an undulating, swooping flight. Usually the flight resembles that of a Pintail, straight with rapid wing-beats, a resemblance accentuated by the slender neck and tail.

The wing-feathers of Ivory-bills are stiff and hard, thus making their flight noisy. In the initial flight, when the wings are beaten particularly hard, they make quite a loud, wooden, fluttering sound, so much so that I often nicknamed the birds 'wooden-wings'; it is the loudest wing-sound I have ever heard from any bird of that size excepting the grouse. At times when the birds happened to swoop past me, I heard a pronounced swishing whistle.

Roosting

Ivory-bills roost in holes or hollows like most or all other woodpeckers. In the Singer Tract, the birds inhabiting John's Bayou area came to roost almost every night in the same area of the woods, and each bird usually used the same hole. The lone male in the Mack's Bayou area frequently used the same roosting hole, but was more erratic than the John's Bayou birds. A. A. Allen (Allen and Kellogg) saw Ivory-bills in Florida returning to the same cypress trees in the evening that they had left that morning.

Roost holes of Ivory-bills resembled nest holes, exteriorly at least; I never examined the interior of one. Audubon (1842) stated that the old nest holes were often used for roosting, but I never saw any of the holes that I knew were once nests to be used for such purposes, and I have seen Ivory-bills digging holes that they later used for roosting. Four roost trees that I knew were green ash and three were Nuttall's oak; two of the ash trees had two holes a piece in the trunk. All of the holes were in dead trees or dead stubs. They were from forty to fifty feet from the ground; the entrance of each was shaped like the entrance to a nest, roughly oval and measuring about four by five inches. The holes did not face in any particular direction and were not located for protection from rain or wind. Plate 14 is a photograph of a roost tree and hole.

The first time that I observed Ivory-bills digging out a roost hole was on April 17, 1937. Three birds, a pair and one young out of the nest a few weeks, came to an almost dead ash tree that was within forty yards of the tree in which the adult male roosted regularly. There were already two holes in the trunk, four feet apart. The female began cleaning out the lower hole, reaching in so far that only her tail projected from the entrance and then swinging back to throw a billful of chips over her shoulder. The male bird worked on the upper hole, pecking and throwing out chips. The pair kept it up for some time while the young bird idled nearby, once curiously examining the work of the female. The young bird used one of these holes for roosting later that year. In March of the following year, when the same pair still had young in the nest, the male of the pair spent some time in digging out a new hole in a live Nuttall's oak about 100 yards from the nest tree. While he was working the female sat nearby. After a while the two birds moved over to another oak, and the female worked out a hole in that tree while the male sat. In between sitting and working on the holes, the adults foraged for themselves and the young bird. About a week after I saw this happen, the male used his hole to roost in, at least once; soon after that he was again using his old roost hole in an ash.

Roost holes of the John's Bayou birds were the center of their range, and were near the nest sites. The male bird usually roosted in a dead ash tree which had two holes in it, usually using the upper hole. Of the twenty-eight times that I watched the male bird's roost hole, twenty times the male roosted there; of the remaining eight, when the male was not there, I heard Ivory-bills call within earshot, and believed that the male roosted nearby on at least four occasions. The female usually roosted about two hundred yards to the northeast of the male's roost hole, but was more erratic than the male in using the same hole.

The young birds that left the nest never, to my knowledge, returned to the nest hole for roosting; for the first few nights they roosted in the open, clinging to a limb or the side of a tree. In 1937 the young bird left the nest on March 31; on April 17 he was in the hole usually used by the adult male, who was in the lower hole of the same tree. Later that season the young bird roosted in the ash tree forty yards northwest of the male's tree, and once the male and the young roosted in separate holes in that second tree. Those two cases of two birds roosting in the same tree were exceptional, and I never saw two birds use the same hole. In 1938 the young bird left the nest on March 19; I did not keep close track of him after that, but on May 10 he was using the ash near the male bird's tree, the same tree used by the young of the preceding year. He continued roosting there right through the nesting season of the following year.

During the summer of 1941 much of the forest in the John's Bayou area was cut over, including the old roosting ground of the Ivory-bills of that area. The tree in which the male had usually roosted was left standing, passed up by the loggers because it was dead and almost rotten; but the male was not roosting there in December 1941, and I do not know where it went. The female, presumably of the same pair, had moved to a hole in a dead oak stub in the virgin timber almost on the edge of the cut-over, and an immature female, probably her daughter of the year, roosted nearby.

The young male Ivory-bill that ranged around Mack's Bayou in 1938 and 1939 had one roost hole that I knew. Of the five times in 1938 that I or Mr. Kuhn watched that hole either late in the evening or early in the morning, the bird roosted there three times. On March 18, 1938, he left that roost hole early in the morning; that afternoon I saw him traveling in a direction away from there, and he did not appear at the roost tree that evening. In 1939 the hole looked worn as if it were being used, and the bird once came from that direction early in the morning, but I did not try to check positively on whether or not the bird was still roosting there.

During the nesting season the male bird incubated or brooded overnight. The female once roosted close by the nest, but at other times disappeared in the direction of her regular roosting place some distance from there. Even though the male had spent every night in the nest during the time the eggs or young were there, on the evening of the day that the young bird left the nest he went to roost in one of his regular roosting holes, like the young forsaking the nest immediately.

The habit of Ivory-bills of using the same roosting holes or roosting grounds most of the time afforded the best means of finding and checking up on the birds during the non-nesting season. When I wanted to observe the birds I always planned to reach the roost ground either at daylight, to watch them leave and then try to follow them, or I would wait there until dusk, to watch the birds come in to the roost. The actions of the birds at these times have already been described in the section on their daily routine.

At about 11 A.M. on April 13, 1937, Mr. Kuhn came to the ash tree which was used for roosting by the male. He glanced up and saw the male bird looking at him from the upper hole in the tree. The male came out and started scolding Kuhn; at that moment the female bird came from the lower hole and joined in the scolding, but she did not come as close to Kuhn as did her mate. A few minutes later the female returned to her same hole while Kuhn was still there. The young bird had been with its parents about a half hour before this happened, but Kuhn saw nothing of it at the time. Kuhn left when the female bird was still in the hole with the male nearby. Three days later, in the roost area, I found the young bird peering from a hole in an almost dead tree, in the late morning. He watched for some time until I got too close, when he came out and climbed up the stub. Several minutes later the female came to the tree and called. These two moved around for half an hour until the male appeared from somewhere, when they all slowly began to travel away. The weather on both of these days was clear and warm.

I found no other case or record of this 'daytime roosting' among Ivory-bills. The only record that is at all comparable is by B. H. Christy (1939), writing of the Pileated Woodpecker: "I saw one of the parent birds reenter at midday a cavity from which the young had recently flown and remain within for forty minutes. Why, I do not know." Ivory-bills and other woodpeckers frequently do not feed during the middle of the day, especially during warm weather, but pass the time quietly. It may be that the birds occasionally retire to roost holes during the middle of the day for safer and more comfortable resting quarters.

Social Habits of the Ivory-bill

Ivory-billed Woodpeckers usually travel in pairs; at least that is the number most often observed. Single individuals seen are usually un-

mated birds. Young birds stay with their parents through the summer and frequently until the following nesting season. These family groups are about the limit of the Ivory-bill's social or flocking tendencies.

Mated birds usually travel and move closely together at all times except during the incubation of the eggs, when one of them must remain on the nest. Even when the John's Bayou birds were caring for young in the nest, they traveled and fed together, and if one started for the nest with a billful of food, the other usually followed even though it carried no food. In traveling and feeding through the woods, the pair would follow each other; neither sex consistently took the lead. Occasionally they traveled quite silently, following each other by sight through several flights. If separated, they would call. Twice the male stayed away from the nest containing young after the female had come to it. The female waited for a while and acted increasingly nervous. Finally she flew to the top of a tall stub that was higher than most tree tops and began to call— *kents*, interspersed with single and double blows on the stub. Soon the male joined her.

The observations of several people, including myself, show that young Ivory-bills stay with their parents through summer and perhaps longer. R. D. Hoyt (1905) states that in Florida the young remain with their parents until December, and that during the summer, groups of three to five Ivory-bills were usually seen, but he never saw more than five. Mr. Kuhn, in the Singer Tract, also saw family groups through the summer and even later. The young bird that the John's Bayou pair in the Singer Tract raised in 1937 was still with its parents in early summer, and their 1938 offspring stayed much longer.

The young birds usually leave or are driven away by the following nesting season, but the single male that was raised by the John's Bayou birds in 1938 stayed in that territory through the following spring. The female of the pair frequently tried to drive him away, but he would only dodge, sulk, and return. The old male paid little or no attention to his yearling son. The young male often fed with the pair while another young was in the nest, and after that young had left the nest, the year-old male frequently traveled with the other three birds. The four birds would travel loosely, not in a close flock; they called little while feeding, but managed to keep together.

Except for such family groups, Ivory-bills seemed to have no desire to move in flocks. On May 11, 1937, Mr. Kuhn found the John's Bayou pair and their young of that year with a second pair of Ivory-bills, but the second pair soon flew off in one direction and the three birds went another. About three weeks later he was following the same three birds, when he heard another Ivory-bill calling repeatedly some distance away. None of the birds he was following answered but continued on in the direction they had been traveling.

There are two records of groups of Ivory-bills together that were more than family groups. W. E. D. Scott (1898) reported seeing in Florida eleven Ivory-bills together, feeding on some girdled timber near a cypress swamp. J. B. Ellis (1917) stated: "Twenty years ago I counted twelve of these birds (Ivory-bills) in a small patch of dead pine trees..." in Florida. In both of these unusual occurrences the woodpeckers were probably attracted together by an abundant food supply.

Voice

A brief description of the voice of the Ivory-billed Woodpecker has already been given, in the section describing the voice as an aid in field identification. The general character of the bird's call, like most sounds difficult to describe with words, can be realized from the descriptions of Audubon (1831), a repeated *pait* resembling the false note of a clarinet; of Chapman (1932), a "high, rather nasal *yap-yap-yap*, sounding in the distance like a penny trumpet"; of Alexander Wilson (1811), a note like the tone of a trumpet or the high note of a clarinet; or of Allen and Kellogg (1937), a *kent* which can be imitated by tooting on the mouthpiece of a clarinet. Hoyt (1905) describes the Ivory-bill's call as weak, resembling the word *schwenk*, while Graham (1909) describes the calls as resembling "the burry reed notes of a Scotch bagpipe."

To my ear, the best description of the Ivory-bill's voice is that the common note is a nasal, yap-like *kent*, with the vowel sound dominant and sounding between the note of a clarinet or saxophone mouthpiece and a tinny trumpet. I took a saxophone mouthpiece into the Singer Tract once, and tooted it while near the Ivory-bills. The sound closely resembled the calls the birds were making, but was flat, lacking the trumpet-like quality; the birds paid no attention to it. Besides the common *kent* note, the Ivory-bill has a more prolonged, upward slurring, repeated *kient-kient-kient* and a lower and softer, and continued *yent-yent-yent* given when mated birds are together during the nesting season. All of the notes have the same nasal, trumpet-like quality. Allen and Kellogg (1937) describe the notes of the female Ivory-bill as being noticeably weaker and less harsh than the male's, but I could not notice a constant difference between the voices of the sexes.

The notes of the nuthatches are the only bird calls I know that sound like the voice of an Ivory-bill; the Ivory-bill's calls are much longer and pitched higher than the calls of a White-breasted Nuthatch, are more in the range of a Red-breasted Nuthatch.

The distance that an Ivory-bill's call can be heard is a disputed subject. Both Audubon and Wilson state that the bird's call is audible for half a mile. Both Hoyt (1905) and Ridgway (1898) describe the bird's call as weak. When Allen and Kellogg (1937) "tested the carrying power of one of our recordings of the common alarm note, *kent*, amplified until it sounded to our ears normal at about one hundred feet, the call was distinctly recognizable at a distance of 2500 feet directly in front of the amplifier with no trees or buildings intervening." The longest distance that I am sure Ivory-bills were heard in the Singer Tract was a little over a quarter of a mile, when Mr. Kuhn heard some birds calling that far away.

The Ivory-bill's notes vary considerably in power, and so do the hearing conditions. The loud *kient-kient-kient* call, given as it often is from the top of a tall tree, on a quiet day with few or no leaves on the trees, could easily be heard for over a quarter of a mile. But some of the conversational notes might hardly carry 200 yards, especially if the foliage were thick.

The vocabulary of the Ivory-bill, if it can be called that, is small. The *kent* note, given in monotone and slowly or infrequently, is the ordinary call note. When the bird is disturbed, the pitch of the *kent* rises, and it is repeated more rapidly, frequently doubled, *kent-kent*, with the second note lower. The prolonged and slurring *kient-kient-kient* call I always heard when two or more birds were together. Several times I saw two or three Ivory-bills climb together to the very top of a dead-topped tree, chorus together a ringing *kient-kient-kient* and then all fly off. I have heard Ivory-bills give this call as one flew in to join its mate, but it is rarely that one will make any call when on the wing. The *yent-yent-yent*, mentioned in a preceding paragraph, was heard only during the nesting season, most often when the Ivory-bills were incubating. It has a conversational tone, and is given by both birds when mates are together; I heard it once when two birds came together and gave the courtship display of touching bills, and it was heard frequently when the Ivory-bills changed places during incubation.

The Laboratory of Ornithology at Cornell University has sound recordings of Ivory-billed Woodpeckers, made in 1935 in the Singer Tract, Louisiana. Most of the calls recorded are the ordinary *kent* and some of the *yent-yent-yent* call given when the birds changed places during incubation. A good series of the *kent* call occurs on the strip of film with footage numbers 8C S91605 to 8C S91572; a good *yent-yent-yent* occurs in 3C S16057 to 062. There is no good recording of the prolonged *kient-kient-kient* call.

The call of a very young Ivory-bill a week or two old was a rapidly repeated *chirp-chirp-chirp*, mostly moderately pitched, occasionally rising in pitch and intensity; it reminded me of the call of a nestling Sparrow Hawk. A nestling bird more fully developed had more of an Ivory-bill tone to his food call; it was a rapidly repeated series of weak nasal calls punctuated by a sharper note, *ehn-ehn-ehn-yeahn'-yeahn'-ehn-ehn-ehn* with a rising inflection on the *yeahn*. When on February 24, 1938, I climbed to an Ivory-bill nest which con-

tained a partly feathered nestling, the bird was silent until I put my hand in the hole, when it emitted a long scraping buzz.

The nestling Ivory-bill of 1938 started giving adult-like *kents* about two weeks before it left the nest; the call was thinner and hoarser than an adult's. The day the young bird left the nest its voice was more like an adult's, but was still thin; it joined the adults in the *kient-kient-kient* call. The young bird continued giving the food call for at least a month after leaving the nest, although the call got progressively lower and coarser. The other calls made by the young bird soon became indistinguishable from those of the adults.

Ivory-bills also signal by pounding with the bill on limbs or stubs, sometimes a single hard blow, but more often a hard, double rap, *bam-bam*, the second note sounding like an immediate echo of the first. They frequently double-rap when disturbed, either by the presence of persons or when one of the pair is absent. Twice I saw the female of a pair mount to a tall dead limb when the male had been absent some time, and call and double-rap for a few minutes until the male returned. The single male in the Mack's Bayou area of the Singer Tract made many single raps, even when it apparently was not disturbed. These single and double raps are surprisingly loud. The birds would often peck or tap until they found a good place, would often move to a hard dead stub, and then strike a resounding single or double blow.

Occasionally I was able to make Ivory-bills answer by imitating their pounding with a club on a hard dead stump or similar place, making either single or double raps as loudly as I could. They sometimes answered with calls, sometimes by pounding. Once I heard some birds rap and pound in response to the chopping of wood.

Thompson (1885) and E. A. McIlhenny (Bendire) describe the Ivory-bill as drumming or rolling like other woodpeckers, but no other writer mentions this, and I have never heard anything resembling a continued drum.

Reactions of the Ivory-bill to Humans

There has long been an idea that Ivory-billed Woodpeckers could not stand civilization, and for some unexplained reason could not endure the trespassing of man in their territory. This idea has frequently been advanced as the reason for the Ivory-bill's decrease. It has probably arisen from descriptions of various writers who have pictured the Ivory-bills as a supremely wary bird. Audubon (1831) stated that in two instances, when he appeared at the foot of the tree in which Ivory-bills were digging a nest, the birds abandoned it.

Arthur T. Wayne wrote in his field catalogue a note under April 22, 1892: "I saw and heard four Ivory-bills the day before in California Swamp, but could not get a shot as they were too wild, and couldn't be approached nearer than 300 or 400 yards." This was in an area where several Ivory-bills had been shot, and these birds could have become wary from shooting. The fact that they were pursued so constantly and avidly by collectors is probably the reason for the wary reputation of the bird.

In my own experience, Ivory-bills have not been particularly shy, certainly not noticeably more wary and wild than the Pileated Woodpecker. When I began following the birds to observe their feeding habits, they at first were shy and alert, watching me, frequently yapping or double-rapping, and not allowing too close an approach. But they rapidly became used to a person and in a day or so would pay little or no attention to one a moderate distance away. I frequently stood almost directly under the tree in which they were feeding without disturbing them.

Around their nest, Ivory-bills became disturbed when intruders first came near, scolding and yapping at them, occasionally coming quite close; but they behaved like most other birds and quickly accepted the presence of people and blinds. The presence of people near or even on the nest tree did not upset them, or even abnormally disturb them. In 1938 I found an Ivory-bill's nest, and a few days later, when I was spiking the tree to reach and examine the nest, the adults suddenly found me half way up the tree. The male bird came to the nest tree, hopped downward and looked me over, and then climbed up and flew to a nearby tree. I went down the tree and moved a few yards away, and the male almost immediately went to the nest, fed the young, and then entered to brood. A short time later the female saw me just as I started down from the nest; she scolded a bit but quickly went to the nest as soon as I had left the tree. Several similar experiences have led me to believe that Ivory-bills behave toward persons as most other birds of similar size do—although they may be shy and wary at first, they become accustomed to and can stand the proximity of man. Certainly in none of my experiences have Ivory-bills deserted a nest or in any way markedly modified their behavior because of the presence of people.

The center of the Ivory-bills' feeding territory in the John's Bayou area was logged during the summer of 1941, tractors, trucks, and men creating much disturbance there. At the time there were at least three Ivory-bills, an adult pair and a juvenal, in the area. By December of that year the adult male had disappeared, where or for cause unknown, but the female and juvenal were still roosting and feeding in the same territory. At least two of the three birds had been little affected by the presence of many men and machines.

Ivory-bills occasionally exhibited curiosity about unusual objects near the nest. Sometimes they flew to the tree in which I had built a blind, and hopped around eyeing the blind. Once I saw the male bird and once the female climb down the nest tree to examine the spikes that I had driven into the trunk. Each of them edged up to a spike and gave it a sharp tap with the bill; it seemed to baffle them and, climbing back up the tree, they cautiously avoided nearing the other spikes.

Plate 15.   Ivory-bill nest tree, a sweet gum.   Singer Tract, La., 1937.

Plate 16. Ivory-bills exchanging places during incubation, the male leaving the nest. April 1935.

Part IV.   Reproductive and Nesting Habits

CHAPTER 12

Territory and Courtship

Territory

IVORY-BILLED Woodpecker pairs usually nest well separated from each other, and at least occasionally nest in the same area year after year; this is the only evidence I know indicating that Ivory-bills have true nesting territories, for there are no records of the birds protecting a territory from trespass by another Ivory-bill.

To my knowledge, the nearest that Ivory-bills have nested to each other in the Singer Tract is about three miles, although it is likely that nests have occurred closer than this because the feeding ranges of different pairs have occasionally been adjacent. Robert Ridgway (1898) describes collecting a male Ivory-bill in southern Florida as it flew from its nest, and then finding another hole two hundred yards from the first which he considered another nest, but he saw no birds near that second hole and it was probably only a roost hole.

In the John's Bayou area of the Singer Tract a pair of Ivory-bills, and apparently the same pair, has nested at least five years; four of the nests of that period were located within a diameter of one thousand yards approximately in the center of their feeding range. Despite the year after year use of the same nesting area by this pair I never saw or heard any evidence of their fighting or in any way protecting their territory. Once, soon after the young had left the nest in the John's Bayou area, a second pair of Ivory-bills came into the area and met the John's Bayou birds, as was described in a preceding section, but there was no suggestion of fighting or antagonism by any of the birds, only indifference. The only times I have ever seen any semblance of fighting among Ivory-bills were when a female occasionally tried to drive away from her vicinity the young bird she and her mate had raised the preceding year. Although Ivory-bills may appear to have nesting territories, like other birds, there is yet no evidence that they defend these territories from other Ivory-bills.

Courtship

The season for courtship of the Ivory-billed Woodpecker varies considerably. R. D. Hoyt (1905) states that in Florida the mating season is in December with nest building beginning in late January. Also, Henry Bryant (1859) states that the genital organs of the specimens he procured from March to May in Florida were "quiescent . . . they would seem to breed very early or very late." But A. A. Allen (Allen and Kellogg) observed a pair courting in central Florida on April 13, 1924. Courtship has not been observed in other parts of the bird's range, but the time is probably erratic everywhere, as the time of nesting has been erratic over the entire range of the bird.

Arthur A. Allen has observed and described (Allen and Kellogg) the courtship procedure of a pair of Ivory-bills in central Florida. About 6 A.M. on April 13, 1924, he and Mrs. Allen watched the pair leave their roost in a group of medium-sized cypress trees. "On the morning of the 13th, they called as they left these cypress trees, and flew to the top of a dead pine at the edge of the swamp where they called and preened. Finally the female climbed up directly below the male and when she approached him closely he bent his head downward and clasped bills with her. The next instant they both flew out on to the 'burn' where we followed their feeding operations for about an hour."

I once saw a somewhat similar performance in Louisiana, on March 13, 1938, when a pair of Ivory-bills had one almost grown, young bird in the nest. The male of the pair fed the young bird and then flew to the female, landing below her on the tree trunk; he climbed up to a position just above her, gave the quiet call which is often exchanged by the birds during the nesting season, and then the two touched bills twice. After that the male moved on up the tree. Perhaps coupled with this return of the courtship performance, for that is what it appeared to be, was the behavior of this pair during the rest of the morning. The two birds spent most of their time near the nest; the female dug in a new hole in an oak for a time while the male sat nearby, and then the two moved to another oak and the male continued his work of digging another hole; this one was subsequently used for a roosting hole by the male.

Ivory-bills probably stay paired throughout the year and mate for life. Audubon (1831) believed that the birds paired for life. No matter what season of the year, Ivory-bills have almost always been observed in pairs, indicating that they do not separate during the non-breeding season.

CHAPTER 13

Nest Building and the Nest

Nesting Records of the Ivory-billed Woodpecker

THE following table summarizes Ivory-billed Woodpecker nesting records, naming in order the locality of the record, the date, location of the nest, the number of eggs or young, and the authority for the record. The records are grouped by states.

Florida

Big Cypress region; Feb. 15, 1897; in cypress 70' up; R. Ridgway (1898).

Manatee Creek, Manatee Co.; no date; in cypress 30' up; Univ. Fla. Museum, Gainesville.

Swamp near Tarpon Springs; March 17, 1880; in large cypress 41' up; one young, "one-third"grown; W. E. D. Scott (1888).

Near Clermont, Lake Co.; March 4, 1904; young in nest; R. D. Hoyt (1905).

Near Clermont, Lake Co.; Feb. 15, 1905; in live cypress 58' up; 2 eggs; R. D. Hoyt (1905).

Second nest of pair referred to above; March 9, 1905; in dead cypress stump 47' up; 2 eggs; R. D. Hoyt (1905) and M.C.Z. collection.

Central Florida; April 6, 1908; in cypress 60' up; 3 nearly full fledged young; O. E. Baynard (1909).

Taylor Creek, Orange Co.; April 13, 1924; cypress 30' up; nest complete; A. A. Allen (Allen and Kellogg).

Lake Harney; 2 eggs; Univ. Fla. collection.

Mouth Withlacoochee River; Jan. 20, 1880; incubating; W. E. D. Scott (1881).

Alachua Co.; young in nest; O. E. Baynard (1913).

Old Town; April 15, 1892; young female about two weeks out of the nest; A. T. Wayne (1893), spec. M.C.Z.

Pumpkin swamp, Dixie Co.; April 19, 1893; bay tree 30' up; 3 eggs; A. T. Wayne (1910, and field catalogue).

Taylor Co.; March 16, 1904; in dead cabbage palm 25' up; young; R. D. Hoyt (1905).

Georgia

Okefenokee region; late March; building in long-dead pine; M. Thompson (1896) (questionable).

Okefenokee region; in long-dead pine; 5 eggs; M. Thompson (1885) (questionable).

Altamaha swamp; April 10, about 1860; 4 eggs; Dr. S. W. Wilson (H. B. Bailey, 1883).

Louisiana

Avery Island; April 9, 1892; 3 fresh eggs; E. A. McIlhenny (Bendire).

Avery Island; May 19, 1892; 4 eggs well incubated; a second set; ditto.

Avery Island; May 2, 1892; cypress 41' up; 3 eggs; ditto.

Tensas swamp, Franklin Parish; July 1899; white elm; 1 young, well feathered; G. E. Beyer (1900).

Singer Tract, Madison Parish; Feb. 17, 1938; red maple 55' up; 1 young, small.

March 26, 1937; sweet gum 70' up; 1 young, almost grown.

March 28, 1939; dead Nuttall's oak 65' up; 1 young, well grown.

April 6, 1935; red maple 43' up; incubating; Allen and Kellogg.

May 10, 1935; dead oak 48' up; small young; Allen and Kellogg.

May 13, 1933; oak 45' up; probably small young; J. J. Kuhn (Allen and Kellogg).

Late May 1936; 4 young just out of nest; J. J. Kuhn.

July 1931; 4 young just out of nest; J. J. Kuhn.

July 1932; 2 young seen by J. J. Kuhn and H. C. Sevier.

July 1933; 2 young seen by J. J. Kuhn.

July 1936; 2 young out of nest; J. J. Kuhn.

June 1938; 2 young out of nest; J. J. Kuhn.

Texas

Neches River bottom, Jasper Co.; May 3, 1885; 40' up; 3 eggs; B. F. Goss (Bendire).

Brazos River; May 1864; young in nest; H. E. Dresser (1865).

Time of Year for Nesting

Ivory-bills vary greatly in their time for nesting. The earliest record is for Florida, a bird incubating on January 20, 1880 (W. E. D. Scott, 1888) near the mouth of the Withlacoochee River. This is earlier than the most southern nesting record, for February 15, 1897, in the Big Cypress region (Ridgway, 1898), although the observer, Ridgway, did not determine whether eggs or young were in the nest. A nest near Clermont, Lake County, in the same part of Florida as the first nest mentioned, had fresh eggs on February 15, 1905 (R. D. Hoyt). In Taylor County, Florida, a nest with young was found on March 16, 1904 (R. D. Hoyt), and in the adjacent county, Dixie, a set of eggs, one with a large embryo, was collected on April 19, 1893, a difference in dates of over a month in the same region. Probably the latest nesting record for Florida is by A. A. Allen (Allen and Kellogg), who found a nest completed but with incubation not yet started on April 13, 1924, in eastern Orange County.

Nesting dates for Louisiana have varied just as much. On February 17, 1938, I found in the Singer Tract, Madison Parish, a nest with a young bird, quite small; the egg was probably laid in late January, and the young bird left the nest on March 19. In the preceding and succeeding years the same pair, in the John's Bayou area, nested within two or three weeks of the same time, for in 1937 I found in the nest one well-grown young on March 26, which left on the 31st, and in 1939 I found the nest of the same pair with one young on March 28, the young flying on April 7. In 1935 a pair of Ivory-bills that were quite likely the same birds were incubating in the area on April 6 (Allen and Kellogg). In 1936 J. J. Kuhn found in that same area four young just out of the nest in late May. Although this last may have been a second attempt at nesting, there was a range of at least two months between the earliest and latest dates for young leaving the nest in the same area. In 1931, in a different part of the tract, Mr. Kuhn saw four very young birds out of the nest in July. Other nesting records for that part of Louisiana can be found in the preceding table. In southern Louisiana, Ivory-bill nests with eggs have been found at Avery Island by E. A. McIlhenny (Bendire) on April 9 and May 2, 1892, and a second nesting on May 19 of that year.

Nesting records for Georgia and Texas are not so variable. M. Thompson (1896) saw a pair building in late March in southern Georgia, and in the Altamaha swamp eggs were collected on April 10 (H. B. Bailey, 1883). The two nesting records for Texas are for a nest with eggs near the lower Neches River on May 3, 1885 (Bendire), and for a nest with young in May 1864 on the Brazos River (Dresser).

Audubon (1831) stated that the Ivory-bill raised two broods in the southern part of its range, but there is no evidence to support this, though it will lay again if the first nest is destroyed, a subject discussed in a later section.

The pair of Ivory-bills in the John's Bayou area was incubating in April of 1935, and must have been incubating in January or February of the years 1937 through 1939, making a difference of at least two months in the time of nesting in the same region; there is the possibility, however, that the April nest was a second attempt. Trying to find some reason for the difference, I secured weather data for this region for the years in question from the U. S. Weather Bureau Station at Vicksburg, Mississippi. Data were secured for December through March of the winter season of each of these years for monthly mean temperature, percentage of possible sunshine, and total precipitation. Of these three groups, the only one in which there was the same difference between the early nesting years, 1937 through 1939, and the late nesting year, 1935, was the percentage of possible sunshine; in the other groups, mean temperature and total precipitation, there was no correlation between the weather and the time of nesting. The relation between the percentage of possible sunshine and the time of nesting is rather surprising, as can be seen from the following table.

PERCENTAGE OF POSSIBLE SUNSHINE,
VICKSBURG, MISS,

Month	1934–35	1936–37	1937–38	1938–39
December	50	31	30	37
January	50	14	41	39
February	54	44	39	39
March	51	51	47	58

In the season of 1935, when the birds nested late, having eggs in April, there was a greater amount of sunshine all through the winter months than during any of the three years when they nested early, except the March figures which could not have had any effect on the time of early nestings. The Ivory-bills nested earliest during cloudy winters. This is at variance with the opinions of some biologists, but it agrees with the observations of Mrs. M. M. Nice (1937), who noted in Song Sparrows that in five out of six breeding seasons the birds nested early in cloudy Aprils and later when there was an excess of sunshine; she considered that the amount of sunshine had no effect on the start of nesting. Linsdale (1933) has shown that, in some areas at least, birds nest when food conditions are best for feeding young. The quantity of food largely affects the ranges and distribution of Ivory-bills, and it may also be the determining factor in time of nest starting, but I know of no facts to support or contradict this supposition.

Pileated Woodpeckers did not nest as early as did the Ivory-bill nor as erratically. In 1937 they were nesting by the last week of March. In 1938 some were building during the first week in March, and apparently one pair began incubating during the second week. Most Pileateds, however, did not begin incubating until the last week of the month. I did not see young out of the nest until April 29.

Location and Description of Nest

Audubon (1831) stated that both birds of a pair work in digging the nest cavity, and Thompson (1896) described a female relieving her mate in the excavation of a new hole. On the other hand, E. A. McIlhenny claimed (Bendire) that the female alone does the work of digging out the nest.

In the Florida region most of the recorded nests have been in living or dead cypress trees, mostly bald cypress judging from the type of swamp inhabited by Ivory-bills. Other trees, mentioned in the preceding table, in which Florida birds have nested are bay (sp. ?) and cabbage palm. M. Thompson (1885) described the birds as nesting in long-dead pine trees in the Okefenokee swamp region.

In northern Louisiana (Singer Tract) nests have been built in red maple, sweet gum, Nuttall's oak, and unidentified oak stubs. In the same region G. E. Beyer (1900) found nests in white or American elm and in overcup oak. E. A. McIlhenny stated (Bendire) that in southern Louisiana the birds build in cypress or tupelo, preferably partly dead. Audubon (1831) wrote that the Ivory-bill prefers ash or "hagberry" (hackberry). This makes twelve reported species of trees in which Ivory-bills have nested. In Florida they obviously prefer bald cypress, but in the hardwood forests of the Mississippi Delta they have nested entirely in various hardwood trees.

In Florida, height of the nests from the ground has averaged 45 feet, with extremes of at least 25 (Hoyt) and 70 (Ridgway, 1898). W. E. D. Scott (1881) described a nest "evidently of this species" in a palmetto trunk 15 feet from the ground.

In Louisiana the nests have averaged 51 feet, between 40 and 70 feet, from the ground.

Almost all the nests I have seen in the Singer Tract, Louisiana, have been located in parts of the woods where the ground was at least partly covered with water during the nesting season, late winter and early spring, before the low places there had dried. I know of no reason for this unless it be that apparently more dead and partly dead trees are standing in these places. The nesting cavities were all dug in dead trees or dead parts of living trees where the wood was a bit punky but still quite hard. The first nest described by Allen and Kellogg (1937) was in the dead top of a partly live red maple, with the entrance 43 feet from the ground and facing north, directly underneath a small broken stub. The second nest was in a large dead oak stub, 47 feet 8 inches up, with the entrance facing east and below the bases of broken off branches. Of the three nests I have found in the Singer Tract, the 1937 nest (Plate 15) was in the dead stub of an otherwise living sweet gum, about 70 feet up and facing east; the 1938 nest was situated in the dead top of a living red maple, 55 feet from the ground and opening westward, and had several small branches both above and below the entrance; and the 1939 nest was in a dead Nuttall's oak trunk, from which all the branches had fallen, facing south and about 55 feet from the ground. This tree appeared to be punky, but the base was very hard and solid.

Audubon (1831) stated that the Ivory-bill carefully chose its nest site for protection from rain, digging below a sheltering limb, but very few nests that have been described by other writers or that I have seen have had any particular protection from the weather.

Audubon (1831) and Thompson (1885) described the entrance hole to an Ivory-bill nest as being round, but the nests described by several other writers and all those I have seen have had oval or irregular entrances. The holes that I have examined in the Singer Tract varied from oval through egg-shaped to nearly triangular (Plates 1 and 16). The smallest recorded hole measured $3^1/_2$ inches (Scott, 1888), the largest, the 1937 nest in the Singer Tract, was $4^3/_4$ by

$5^3/_4$ inches, and the most elongate measured $3^1/_4$ by $6^3/_4$ inches (R. D. Hoyt).

For comparison, the entrance holes of Pileated Woodpecker nests are described by Bendire (1895) to be from 3 to $3^1/_2$ inches in diameter.

The shallowest nests described were 14 inches deep (Hoyt), although Audubon gave a minimum depth of 10 inches. The deepest nest is described by M. Thompson (1885) to have been 5 feet deep, and he adds that the depths of nest holes vary from 2 to 9 feet. In the Singer Tract the cavities were from $17^1/_2$ to 25 inches in depth, with an average of 20 inches including the nests described by Allen and Kellogg. The average depth of all Ivory-bill nests that obviously have been carefully measured is 19 inches. The smallest inside diameter, 7 inches, was reported by Audubon (1831), and the largest was for the 1937 nest, $10^1/_2$ inches; the nest cavities I have examined were not radially symmetrical, so the inside measurements depended on how they were taken. The largest measured diameter of the tree at the level of the nest was 22 inches (Allen and Kellogg), and the smallest was 13 inches for both the 1937 and 1938 nests.

The important measurements of the nest cavities excavated by one pair of Ivory-bills in three successive years, in the John's Bayou area of the Singer Tract, are shown in the following table, and Fig. 21 is a diagram made from the average measurements to show the cavities' general shape.

MEASUREMENTS OF IVORY-BILL NEST CAVITIES, SINGER TRACT, LA. EXCAVATED BY THE SAME PAIR OF BIRDS

(measurements in inches)

Year	Entrance hole	Depth	Inside diameters	Diameter of stub at nest
1937	$4^3/_4 \times 5^3/_4$	25	$8^1/_2 \times 10^1/_2$	13
1938	$4^1/_4 \times 5$	$17^1/_2$	6×9	13
1939	$4 \times 5^1/_2$	20	6×9	14
Average	4.3×5.4	20.8	6.8×9.5	13.3

1937: in dead stub of living sweet gum 70 feet up.
1938: in dead top of living red maple 55 feet up.
1939: in dead Nuttall's oak trunk 55 feet up.

The inside diameter from side to side of the cavity is greater than from front to back.

R. D. Hoyt (1905) and F. M. Phelps (1914) remark that the bark around the entrance of nests in cypress trees is shredded or stripped from the trunk for a considerable distance. Nest trees I have seen in the Singer Tract had quite a bit of bark scaled off here and there and especially at the top of the stub. Much of this bark was dislodged when the birds struck hard single or double blows as they often do when alarmed, and some was loosened by the birds idly pecking at the bark as they do when feeding. Shredding of the cypress bark was probably done in this way, and that below the nest hole could have been roughened by the birds climbing up the trunk.

CHAPTER 14

Eggs and Incubation

Description and Numbers of Eggs

THE best description of eggs of the Ivory-bill has been written by Charles Bendire (1895): "The eggs of the Ivory-billed Woodpecker are pure china white in color, close grained, and exceedingly glossy, as if enameled. They vary in shape from an elongate ovate to a cylindrical ovate, and are more pointed than the eggs of most of our Wood-peckers. They appear to me to be readily dis-tinguished from those of the Pileated Woodpecker, some of which are fully as large."

Sets of Pileated eggs have apparently been la-beled 'Ivory-billed,' sometimes deliberately, and consequently there is much confusion about the size of Ivory-bill eggs.

For the Ivory-bill, Bendire gives 34.87 by 25.22 mm. as the average of thirteen eggs, the largest measured being 36.83 by 26.92, and the smallest 34.54 by 23.62. Two sets of two eggs each collected by R. D. Hoyt (1905), not included in Bendire's figures, averaged 36.5 by 27.6 mm. B. H. Christy (1939) gives 33.16 by 25.21 mm. as

being the average measurement of Pileated eggs, with the largest egg of that species measuring 38.2 by 27.1 mm.

The number of eggs or young, where that has been reported for each nesting record, is given in the table of nesting records. Of these, 5 nests had 1 young each, 3 had 2 eggs, 5 had either 3 young or 3 eggs apiece, for 4 there were either 4 eggs or 4 young in a brood, and 5 eggs were re-ported by M. Thompson (1885) for 1 nest. Audu-bon (1831) stated that 6 eggs were laid in a nest, but there is no evidence to support this. Three of the 5 nests with 1 young apiece were examined by the writer, and there was no evidence of there ever having been more than 1 egg. The average of the data which have just been listed is 2.6 eggs or young per nest; the average number of eggs alone is 2.9 per nest.

The relation between the number of eggs or young and the time of year is shown in the follow-ing table for the records where those data are reported.

Fig. 21. Diagram of Ivory-bill nest cavity, using average measurements in inches.

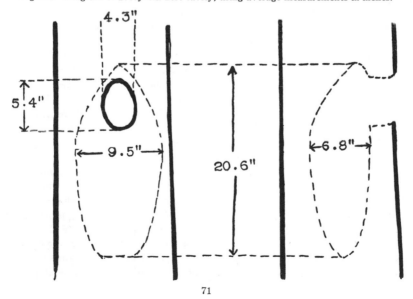

NUMBER OF NESTS RECORDED FOR EACH MONTH IN
RELATION TO NUMBER OF EGGS OR YOUNG

Month and stage of nesting	Number of eggs or young for nest			
	1	2	3	4
February, young	2	...	...	...
February, eggs	...	1	...	...
March, young	2	...	...	...
March, eggs	...	1 (2nd set)	...	...
April, young	...	...	1	...
April, eggs	...	...	2	1
May, young	1	...	...	1
May, eggs	...	...	2	1 (2nd set)
July, young just out	...	...	...	1

Early nests had decidedly fewer eggs and young than did later nests. The only exception is the one nest with a single young in May (in Louisiana, Beyer, 1900). Nests which must have had eggs in January or February had one or two, while nests which did not have eggs until April or May had three or four, with the one exception mentioned. The data were tested by the chi square method and the variation in size of sets between early and late dates was significant; there is little probability that the numbers obtained were due to chance. There are both Florida and Louisiana records for the small early sets and the larger late sets, so the differences are not due to location of the nests.

Schmaus (1938) has shown that the size of the egg clutch of some species of birds varies with the abundance of food, and there may be a seasonal increase in the food supply of the Ivory-bill in April and May that results in the bird laying more eggs then.

Incubation

No Ivory-bill nest has ever been observed through the entire period of incubation, so the exact length of the period is unknown. Eggs of the Pileated Woodpecker hatch in 18 days (Christy, 1939, and J. S. Y. Hoyt, MS.), and since Ivory-bill eggs are larger, they probably require about 20 days. Incubation is by both sexes, the male doing most of it, as he stays on the nest overnight.

The only extensive observations and records of the Ivory-bill's activities during incubation were made in the Singer Tract in 1935 by A. A. Allen, P. P. Kellogg, and the writer; observations made there are reported fully by Allen and Kellogg (1937).

This nest was in the dead top of a red maple 43 feet from the ground. It was found on April 6, 1935, by J. J. Kuhn, A. A. Allen, G. M. Sutton, and the writer, and the birds were then incubating. Even this sudden intrusion by four people did not markedly disturb them and interrupted their setting for but a few minutes. On April 9, a small camp was made about 300 feet from the nest, equipment was set up there for sound recording of the Ivory-bills, and a blind was built in a tree about twenty feet from the nest for photography. Professor Allen and Dr. Kellogg stayed at the camp from then until April 14, when the sound records, motion and still pictures were made of the birds. For the four days from April 10 through 13 a continuous record was kept of the activities of the pair about the nest, with the aid of a pair of 24× binoculars at the camp-site focused on the nest. Activities about the camp and near the nest tree did not seriously affect the birds. They quickly, rather surprisingly so, accepted the presence of from two to five people, the blind, and the microphone with its large reflector, and most of the time behaved in a seemingly normal manner.

The incubating bird was completely invisible inside the cavity. Occasionally it would peer out of the entrance, especially if there was any noise outside. The female did this once when a Carolina Wren came down the tree to a point just above the hole, and once when a Red-bellied Woodpecker climbed past the nest. Several times in the four days the incubating bird came out and climbed around the tree for a few moments, sometimes when all was quiet and again when its mate called nearby.

At times the birds changed places on the nest with a regular ceremony. One would fly or climb to the entrance and signal the other by calling or pounding. We occasionally heard the setting bird answer by pounding on the inside of the cavity. It would flip out of the hole and catch itself on the outside of the tree beside its mate, and the pair would then exchange a low, almost musical call that had a conversational quality, often given with their bills pointed upward (Plate 16). Then the one bird would climb up the tree to fly off while the other entered the nest. At other times they changed places silently, one even leaving the nest before the second reached the tree. The birds entered the hole head first, then often turned to peer out for a moment before settling to incubate.

The bird off the nest frequently fed nearby, for we often would hear it calling. They were not followed persistently, however, to determine their regular feeding range at this time.

The male Ivory-bill stayed on the nest every night. During the day the female incubated most of the time; for the four days she averaged six and a half hours on the nest to three and a half for the male. They exchanged places generally about eight times a day. There was no regularity in the lengths of the times spent on the nest, except that the female generally incubated longest when she first relieved the male in the morning and then just before the male took his place for the night. Periods spent on the nest in the daytime varied from twenty minutes to over three and a half hours. The earliest that the female relieved her mate in the morning was 5:35 A.M., the latest, 7:30; the earliest that the male went on the nest for the night was about 3:30 P.M., and the latest was 5:45. At that season, it began to get light about 5 A.M. and dark about 7 P.M.

When the birds were disturbed by our presence, they changed places more often, but they rarely left the eggs uncovered. The only times they stayed away from the nest were twice on April 11, for a total of a little more than an hour and a half. They quickly accepted the building of a blind near the nest, returning almost immediately after the blind was placed in a nearby tree. Our photographing disturbed them more, with movements within the blind and the sound of a motion picture camera. The female was decidedly the more nervous of the two, and it was primarily her timidity that caused the eggs to be uncovered for a time. They soon lost their fear, however, and at least once the male entered the hole when a person was climbing from the blind only twenty feet from the nest hole. They finally became so accustomed to disturbance that noise at the base of the tree did not even cause them to look out.

When we left the nest on April 14, the birds were behaving normally. On April 29, Mr. Kuhn visited the nest and found the pair peering into the hole, going inside for a few moments, and then flying to nearby trees where they preened and scratched. On May 9, Professor Allen returned to the nest with Mr. Kuhn and Dr. L. M. Dickerson, and found it deserted. Cutting it down, they discovered bits of egg shells mixed with the chips in the nest and an abundance of mites. The possible causes for the failure of this and other nests are discussed in the later section, 'Discussion of Causes for Nesting Failures.'

CHAPTER 15

Care of Young in Nest

No Ivory-bill nest of my knowledge has ever been observed at the time the eggs hatched, so the behavior of the birds then is not known, nor is the period that young birds stay in the nest. On February 17, 1938, I found a nest with the old birds feeding young. One week later I climbed to the nest, when the old birds were away, to examine its contents. I could just reach the bottom of the nest with the tips of my fingers, and found just one young bird. I gently probed under and around him but could feel no other objects of any kind in the nest except the fine chips at the bottom. The cavity was very warm. The young bird appeared to me to be half grown, and its tail feathers were about one and a half inches long. J. S. Y. Hoyt has found (MS.) that young Pileated Woodpeckers have rectrices that long when they are fourteen days old, so I assume that the young Ivory-bill was about that age on February 24, and that it hatched around the 10th. This young left the nest on March 18 or 19, so it spent a total of about thirty-six days, or a little over five weeks, in the nest.

The only published observations of the activities of Ivory-bills with young in the nest were made by Professor A. A. Allen (Allen and Kellogg), who watched a nest in the Singer Tract in 1935 for a few hours. My own observations of their habits with young were made in the Singer Tract on single nests in each of the three years from 1937 through 1939; each nest contained but one young. The birds' activities were watched part of the time from blinds built on the ground or in trees near the nest tree. Observations were not made continuously because at times I decided it was better to stay away rather than risk too much disturbance which might cause desertion, and because I spent much time in other areas of the tract trying to find new nesting pairs. Because I have no large number of continuous observations, I have made no attempt to analyze in detail the behavior of the woodpeckers in caring for the nestlings, but have described only their general behavior.

On March 3, 1938, I spent an entire day from dawn to dusk at this nest keeping an accurate record of all the activities of the adult birds, watching them from a blind built near the foot of the nest tree, and from spots nearby where I could be inconspicuous. The following is an account of their activities on that day, with comments introduced from other days' observations to assist in describing the general routine and manner of the adults caring for the young bird.

The nest was in the dead top of a living red maple tree; it was located fifty-five feet from the ground and faced west. Near the nest were some large sweet gum, Nuttall's oak, and American elm trees, and a little in front of the nest were several medium-sized green ashes. The undergrowth near the nest tree was a tangle of Smilax and other vines, and the ground was partially covered with shallow pools of water. Leaves were beginning to appear on most trees.

March 1 was a bright sunny day, quite warm, with little wind. At six o'clock in the morning it was just light enough to see to walk, and Cardinals began singing, followed by Carolina Wrens, Tufted Titmice, Towhees, and Red-bellied Woodpeckers.

March 1, 1938:
6:25. The male Ivory-bill's head appeared at the nest entrance a time or two, then he thrust it out. Just after that I heard the young bird call a bit. The female flew in, without calling, to a tree back of the blind. Just about 6:30 the male slipped out of the hole and flew to the female. They talked a few seconds in the soft notes used at nest exchange, then flew west together.
6:51. The sun peeped through the trees.
7:50. The female came and fed the young without calling. The nestling called loudly, the tip of its bill showing at the entrance. The female flew east a short distance, called from there.

The usual procedure in bringing food to the young was for the adult with food to fly to a tree in the vicinity of the nest, often a tall slender ash about thirty yards away. Then it flew to the nest tree and climbed up to the left of the entrance. There were two small branches below the hole, making the birds approach the nest from the left or north side of the tree; the bark on that side was worn so smooth that they often had trouble clinging there. Then it sidled around and paused just below the hole, looking sharply from side to side. It went up to the hole, peered in, and then half entered, so that only the rear part of the body was visible. It usually emerged and reentered three or four times. Often it seemed to be jerking as though working food from the back of its mouth. Leaving, it climbed to the top of the stub and flew, often stopping on a nearby tree before going on. Once or twice, on February 17, 1938, when the young bird was probably only a week old, the adults entered the nest completely to feed. All other times they fed by reaching into the cavity from the entrance.

The young bird almost always called whenever it heard the adults on the outside of the tree; its food call has been described in the section, 'Voice.' Later, when the nestling was larger, it frequently sat looking from the entrance and would call whenever it saw an adult nearby. It always retired within the nest and below the level of the entrance before taking food.

7:54. Female again fed young, no call from her but the young was vociferous.

8. Male came with food, fed young without calling. He entered the nest for a moment, reappeared with excreta in his bill, flew over the blind so I could not see what he did with it. A moment later the female fed the nestling a grub about one and a quarter inches long, flew southeast, called from there.

8:10. Female came quietly, fed young which called, and left.

8:17. Male quietly came, fed the young with about a two-inch grub, and immediately after him the female came with a small grub and fed the young.

8:20. Female came without making a sound, entered the hole for a moment, came out and flew off.

8:33. Male came and quietly fed nestling, which called less loudly now.

8:45. Male brought a small grub, fed young quietly.

A few minutes before 9 one bird started calling a short distance from the nest; the other, nearby, answered with a double-rap. The two rapped and double-rapped several times, then moved off. From the blind I could see nothing to disturb them.

9:25. Male brought food, called once, fed young. Movement in the blind disturbed the female not far from the nest. She started yapping. The male answered by a double-rap, flew to the female; both called for a minute or more, then went off.

(Two days later, March 3, I followed the pair as they went off on one of their longer feeding trips. On this morning they started a few minutes after 9 and flew through the woods in several flights for a half mile westward. There they slowed their traveling, but did not seem to be much interested in feeding. The female pecked sporadically at hackberry and Nuttall's oak. About 10 o'clock they suddenly and swiftly started back, and about ten minutes later I found them feeding on a dead oak trunk a short distance west of the nest tree. I saw the female secure a grub from the tree, put it in the back of her mouth, and continue scaling away bark after more food. A few minutes later she flew to the nest and fed the young bird.)

9:50. Female returned when I was just outside the blind. She stopped at the ash tree, yapped at me, and then went to feed the young, taking longer than when not disturbed. She returned to ash, called, and the male joined her. Both started feeding nearby.

10:03. Female fed young quietly, young calling very little.

10:08. Female again fed young.

10:32. Male fed young quietly.

10:33. Female fed nestling quietly, apparently feeding it first a one-and-a-half-inch grub held lengthwise in her bill, then bringing a second from the back of her mouth.

Both birds remained in the ash until 10:45, when the male flew to the hole and entered. Female sat for a time on the nearest ash, then busied herself scaling on the elm and gum near the nest.

12:09. Female to nest; the male thrust his head out, and the two 'talked' in low tones. Then she flew off and he retired.

12:15. The male quietly slipped out and flew to the sweet gum.

12:25. Female fed young, which called some. The male sat on the sweet gum for some time and then flew.

12:50. I was standing near the blind when the male flew to a nearby tree, called. The female flew to the nest, apparently fed young, and then flew east a short distance while the male remained in the elm. About a minute later the female flew westward and landed in a tree about eighty yards away. The male then flew after her, passed her, and disappeared through the trees. The female followed him—all this flying without a call.

1:45. Male came, looked in hole, perhaps fed young. He entered hole for about four minutes, and then came out and flew.

2:06. Female came to the tree, low down. She inspected one of the spikes I had used in climbing the tree, gave it several inquisitive, ringing taps. Then she climbed up, giving wide berth to two other spikes. The young called, but she flew off before reaching the nest.

2:07. Male came and sat in the elm near the nest. Female called and dug in a tree just south of nest.

2:22. Female came and fed young quietly; male followed immediately and fed young a one-and-a-quarter-inch grub. Young called rather loudly.

2:55. Male came and fed a big two-inch grub to young, entered hole.

3:17. Female came without food, called from nest tree, climbed up and began digging on far side of tree just below the nest, then flew.

4:10. Female came with food. Male left. She fed young and then flew off to south, called there, and male went toward her.

4:58. Male brought a medium-sized grub, fed it to young, which called loudly and reached his bill up to the entrance. Male was quiet.

5:03. Female swooped in, quickly and quietly fed young, then climbed to top, double-rapped, flew off.

5:18. Male quietly fed young, climbed to the top, sat a moment and then flew off.

5:26. Female quickly fed young and flew off.

5:50. The sun left the tops of the trees.

6:03. The pair of Ivory-bills suddenly flew over the tree tops from the southeast and swung into the dead top branches of a tall sweet gum. The male started feeding a little. The female quietly flew off to a slender dead ash stub about 100 yards from the nest, where she double-rapped once, quickly entered a hole about fifty feet from the ground. A moment later the male flew to the nest, where the young called. The adult Ivory-bill called several times, and then entered.

That seemed to be the signal for the frogs and toads to start singing.

On this day, March 1, 1938, the male parent fed the nestling thirteen times, and the female seventeen times. Of all the times I have seen Ivory-bills feed young, the male did it seventy-seven times and the female eighty-two, showing that the sexes share just about equally in feeding the young bird in the nest. The adults sometimes came in singly, sometimes together, both carrying food, and frequently the pair came to the nest even though only one brought food.

The routine of bringing food to the young followed the general pattern of March 1st throughout the 1938 season and in other years. There was usually a period of active feeding from about 8:30 until 10 or 11, then a lull until the middle of the afternoon, followed by another period of feeding, but not quite as active as in the morning, until 5 o'clock. This pattern was far from inflexible, however, for both repeated feedings and long intervals between feeding occurred at all times of the day. As the nestling grew older, it was fed less often, and just before leaving the nest it was fed on the average of less than twice an hour or about fifteen times a day. The longest time that I observed between feedings occurred on March 30, 1937, just the day before the young bird left the nest, a period of three hours and forty minutes between 11 and 2:40.

On May 10, 1935, Professor A. A. Allen, Dr. L. M. Dickerson, and J. J. Kuhn visited an Ivory-bill nest in a dead oak stub located in the Mack's Bayou area of the Singer Tract. The nest contained young that must have been very small, for when the old birds came with food they entered the nest completely and they apparently had trouble feeding large grubs to the nestling. The food calls were a weak buzzing. The adults brought food six times between 10:45 and 12:30. This nest was destroyed before further observations could be made upon it; its history is discussed more fully in the section treating the causes of nest failure.

The male bird always brooded overnight, and did almost all of the brooding done in the daytime. In 1938 it regularly entered the nest to brood about 11 A.M., staying for a varying period. The longest time I ever knew him to stay on the nest was on March 1 when he remained for one and a half hours. In the afternoons he occasionally brooded for a few minutes at a time. Later in the season the young bird was covered less frequently and for shorter intervals, and during the few days preceding its departure, I never saw it brooded except at night. The only times I saw the female bird enter the nest as if to brood were when the nestling was small, and then she remained but a short time. A. A. Allen also describes (Allen and Kellogg) a female Ivory-bill entering a nest containing small young and remaining inside for a few moments; apparently the only times the female does attempt to brood is when the young are small.

After entering the nest to brood, the male usually paused to look out a few times before settling down. Once, on March 9, 1938, from a blind in a tree, I could see his tail straight up against the back wall of the nest as he covered the young. Occasionally he interrupted his sitting to peer out of the hole.

The nest was cleaned of droppings of the nestling by the male bird, who sometimes dropped them directly from the nest entrance, and sometimes carried them a short distance in his bill, dropping them in flight. The nest was kept clean but not perfectly so, as every nest I examined after the young had left contained a few dried, white droppings mixed with the chips at the bottom.

About 2 P.M. on February 23, 1938, the female came and fed the young, then, sitting at the hole, reached in and began to chop and dig with her bill at the lower edge of the entrance; she would chop four to six times, stop to look around, and then begin again. She did this for about fifteen minutes, then entered the nest and worked around the entrance from the inside. She continued this until almost 3.30, when she climbed out and up to the top of the tree, the young bird calling as she left. This is the only time I saw this happen, and I do not know why she did it.

The adults always were disturbed and excited whenever I first found a nest and they saw me near it. They would call *kents* nervously and loudly, and often double-rapped or pounded on stubs or limbs of the nest tree and nearby trees. As they became accustomed to me, my presence did not disturb them enough to interrupt their activities, but they always called more frequently if they knew I was near. Instances when the birds were disturbed at the nest have been described in an earlier section, 'Reactions of the Ivory-bill to Humans'; in my experience the birds have not been particularly shy around the nest nor seriously upset by the presence of people or of blinds.

After I had spiked the 1938 nest tree, I decided to try to band the young bird so that I could identify him in the field in following years. On March 6, 1938, J. J. Kuhn and I went to the nest to do this. About 10.30 we saw the adults feed the nestling and then leave on a long flight. Immediately I climbed the tree to the nest. Just as I reached toward the entrance the youngster jumped, but he jumped right into my hand and I caught him. He struggled and squalled some, but I had little trouble in putting a band on his left leg. I returned him to the nest, and then started to cut off the branch which obscured the nest hole, so that I could get better pictures of the nest from the blind in a nearby tree. Just as I loosened the branch and threw it down, the young woodpecker again jumped from the nest and fluttered to the ground. He landed in a tangle of vines, where he hung, squalling and calling.

Down the tree I went, as fast as I could, and picked up the young bird. Handing him to Kuhn, I started to take photographs of the bird. Kuhn first held it in his hands. Then it perched on his wrist, lengthwise as on a limb. It had ceased calling by then, but it was scared and viewed me with great distrust. It climbed up Kuhn's arm bit by bit until it reached his shoulder, where it sat for some time and there gave a few sharp taps on his cap. Kuhn raised his hand once, and the youngster hit it hard enough to break the skin.

On upward it climbed until it was perched on the cap. It held its head back and crest on end, making the head look large. The wings were occasionally extended to keep its balance or, when one of us reached toward it, as if it wanted to appear more imposing. Its appearance can be seen from Plates 17 and 18. The birds eye was a dark brown and the bill chalky white. The white tips to all the primaries can be seen in the photographs.

When I had used all my film, I wrapped the young bird in two handkerchiefs, put it inside my shirt, and climbed again to the nest. It struggled a bit, but stopped before I reached the top. Once there, I slipped it into the nest hole, and this time it stayed. This was about 11:30.

Kuhn and I retired a short distance and sat down to wait. At 11.55 the female returned, and hesitated some before going to the entrance, perhaps because of the missing branch. As soon as she looked into the cavity, the young bird called. The male bird did not return until 1:05, when he brought a big mouthful of food, and after feeding entered to brood. I saw the banded woodpecker over a year later, and the band was plainly visible through binoculars.

In two of the nests I have watched, the young bird showed signs of preparing to leave the nest before doing so. On March 31, 1937, the young bird came out of the nest early in the morning and climbed around the stub near the nest. He was fed once by the male at the top of the stub. He handled himself with assurance, pecking at the wood and often peering into the hole. At 8 o'clock the male parent came and called from a tree twenty yards away, and the youngster flew to him to be fed. It did not return to the nest tree after that.

On the afternoon of March 17, 1938, the young bird in the nest of that year was fed several times between 2:30 and 4; each time it acted as though it wanted to come out, and once or twice it almost did. After 4, it did not try so hard. On the afternoon of the 19th I found that young bird with its parents about fifty yards from the nest. In 1939, the nestling suddenly left on April 7, without giving any warning by its actions, although I had been expecting it for some time because of its size.

Care and Development of Young after Leaving Nest

At two of the Ivory-bill nests I watched I was present when the young bird left the nest. At about 6:30 on March 31, 1937, the young bird was at the top of the nest stub, where the parents came to feed it. It climbed around the stub near the nest, and a few times peered into the hole. At 8 o'clock the male parent landed in a nearby tree and called, and the young woodpecker unhesitatingly launched himself into the air and flew from the stub about twenty yards to that tree. The male almost immediately came toward me and began scolding and double-rapping. Soon he was joined by the female, and the pair called nearby for several minutes. A little later the male flew to the nest hole and peered within, then flew off. At 9 o'clock the female flew to the nest and looked in, then she heard the young bird call behind her, and flew to it with food. Soon the male went again to the nest and then to the young bird. Both adults moved off and the youngster followed for a short distance.

Late in the afternoon the young bird was being fed regularly by the adults; it followed its parents around and often pecked in the same places where they had been working. The adults sometimes gave the long call, *kient-kient-kient* and the young tried to join them in the chorus. At 5:30 in the afternoon it fed for the last time, and soon after that the adults began to move toward their roosting ground. The young bird roosted that night in the branches of a sweet gum.

I did not see the nestling of 1938 leave, but it was still in the nest late in the afternoon of March 17, and at 3:15 in the afternoon of the 19th I found it and its parents about fifty yards from the nest. It behaved and was fed just like the bird of the preceding year. It occasionally took fairly long flights, usually slanting downward, and then the adults would fly to it immediately. They did not move far away at any time until about 6:15, when it was dusk and they started for their roosts.

The young bird was left in an oak tree, where it clung upright and closely against the trunk, its bill apparently tucked underneath the scapulars.

The nestling of 1939 left the nest rather abruptly on the afternoon of April 7, without having acted as though it were preparing to leave. I was in the tree blind at the time, securing photographs of the adults as they came to the nest. The adults had fed the young bird regularly until 4:30, then had sat quietly nearby until just after 5, when the male flew to the top of the nest stub and rapped there. A few minutes later I heard a whistle of wings, and the young bird passed the blind, flying about twenty yards on a downward slant to the trunk of a tree. The adult flew to the same tree for a moment, and then the male went to the empty nest, looked in, and entered to stay for a minute or more. Coming out, it returned to the tree where the young was perched. The female soon brought food to it.

I had just started to dismantle the blind in the tree, as it no longer would be useful with the nest empty, when the year-old male Ivory-bill that had remained in the area flew in and joined the pair. When I took the blind from over me, the three adult Ivory-bills began calling and flew to trees near me where they *kented* loudly and rapidly. It was a bit disconcerting to be perched in the crotch of a tree with three big woodpeckers calling so noisily just a few feet away. I covered myself again with the blind and the birds quickly quieted, the pair joining the young which had moved a little farther off during the disturbance. Several minutes later I was able to remove both the blind and myself from the tree without disturbing the birds.

The young woodpecker climbed up into the small branches of a medium-sized ash. The adults first tried to entice it away, but it only stayed and yapped thinly. It was then offered food by the female, but it had trouble handling itself among the twigs and small branches and would not eat. Soon after that it disentangled itself from the tree top and swooped down to a larger limb. The adults made short flights in the vicinity, calling occasionally, until 6:05, when they started flying north toward the roosting area. The young bird had again climbed into the small branches of an ash; it called some, then became quiet. I left it there in the gathering darkness.

The general appearance of a nestling Ivory-bill can be seen from the photographs (Plates 17 and 18) made on March 6, 1938, about twelve days before the bird left the nest, for the young wood-pecker appeared little different when it did leave. The young bird just out of the nest resembled a female Ivory-bill in pattern; the only differences in the plumage were that the young bird had white tips to all the primaries, instead of just to the inner ones, the crest was short, and the tail was short and square. The juvenal's eye was a dark sepia, and the eyelids reddish. The bill was chalky white, and in very young birds there was a dark mark along the culmen.

The development of the juvenal is illustrated in Plate 18. One month after leaving the nest the crest had grown but was still blunt and ragged, the tail had lengthened and the two central tail-feathers were noticeably longer than the others. The eye was beginning to appear lighter in color, and the bill was almost an ivory-white, but still paler than that of an adult.

At two and a half months the first scarlet feather appeared in the head of the 1938 juvenal, but the crest was still blunt. The shape of the tail and colors of the eye and bill were much like those of an adult, but were still recognizably different. At three and a half months the white wing tips to the primaries were worn away, and the young woodpeckers were unrecognizable from adults except for the smaller amount of red and the slight raggedness of the crest and whole plumage.

Both in 1937 and 1938 young Ivory-bills were males. In 1939 I left the tract before any scarlet feathers could have appeared in the crest, so I do not know the sex of that year's bird. In December 1941, on a short visit to the Singer Tract, I found in the same area an adult female accompanied by a single young female raised that year.

Several of the Ivory-bill specimens collected at all seasons of the year have had white tips to some of the outer primaries, beyond the seventh from the end which is usually the primary on which the white begins. It is quite likely that this is a carry-over from the juvenal plumage and is a sign of youthfulness in the Ivory-bill.

The juvenal Ivory-bill just out of the nest im-mediately began accompanying its parents on feeding trips, making short flights from tree to tree. The adults moved away from the young bird frequently, but soon returned to it. The longest that they stayed away was for an hour and a quarter in the middle of the day, while the young bird sat quietly in one spot. It was fed equally by both parents, often as much as fifteen times in an hour, but not steadily throughout the day as their activities usually slowed around noon. On April 2, 1937, the adults worked irregularly for over two hours in and near one tree. The female would climb out on a limb, debarking it for grubs, with the young right behind her giving the food call, and every few minutes she would secure a grub, turn and feed it to the youngster. The male was working nearby, and he would fly to the same limb to feed the young bird, and then return to his working. Food was passed from adult to young by interlocking their opposed bills, in the same way as bitterns and herons feed their young. Occasionally the young bird pecked and poked at the limb with his bill.

Around 6 in the evening the adults usually began to move toward their roost holes. For the first few nights at least, the juvenal stayed behind and did not go to roost in a hole. On the evening of March 22, 1938, three or four days after the young had left the nest, it remained in a leafy-topped oak where it was well hidden. The earliest that I have seen a young bird use a roost hole was on the morning of April 17, 1937, a little more than two weeks after its departure from the nest, when one of the adults emerged from a hole in a dead ash and a few minutes later the young bird came from another hole a little higher in the same stub. The next time I saw this young bird at a roosting hole, it was in another ash a short distance away.

The ability of the bird to fly and keep up with the adults increased rapidly, and within two weeks it accompanied them almost all of the time. The feeding range increased with the young Ivory-bill's powers of flight, and on April 23, 1939, sixteen days out of the nest, the young traveled with the adults about one and one half miles from the roosting ground before 8 in the morning.

The young woodpecker followed its parents as

they fed, and often pecked along the edges of the scaling they had made. Gradually it increased the vigor of its pecking. The earliest that I saw one find food for itself was about four weeks after leaving the nest. At the age of two to two and a half months, the juvenal was still giving the food call and was fed by the adults, although it also found food for itself. On July 14, 1937, when the young bird had been out of the nest for three and a half months, it fed itself regularly, but still gave a subdued food call whenever it was near its parents.

The time when the young Ivory-bills separate from their parents is rather indefinite. R. D. Hoyt (1905) stated that the young stay with the adults until the following mating season in December. J. J. Kuhn has seen groups of Ivory-bills in winter and fall that were probably family groups. On the other hand, in December of 1937 I found a pair in the John's Bayou area of the Singer Tract still using the same roosting ground, but the young bird was not with them. The following spring J. J. Kuhn and I found a single male Ivory-bill in the Mack's Bayou area. It seemed a bit smaller than normal and had some extra white on the tips of the outer primaries, so I believed it to be a young bird. It may well have been the male raised the preceding year by the John's Bayou pair.

In 1938 the young bird of that year was still using the same area but was not always traveling with his parents by August, for on August 8 I saw the pair by themselves and on the 16th I saw the young bird come in alone to the roost ground. In 1939 this male bird was still in the same area, even though his parents had a new nest with young, and he roosted in the same hole he had used since the previous spring. He frequently accompanied the old birds, even flying with them to near the nest, but also traveled alone, going much beyond the usual range of the old birds. The female of the pair occasionally tried to drive him away, but the male apparently paid no attention to him. He was quite easily identified by the band I had placed on his leg the previous year.

A young female raised in 1941 was still with the female parent in December, although the male parent was no longer around.

Plate 17. Young Ivory-bill taken from the nest to band.

Plate 18.   Nestling Ivory-bill, March 6, 1938, twelve days before leaving nest.

Head and tail, one month after leaving nest.

x 2/5. April 28, 1937.

Head, three and one-half months after leaving nest.

x 2/3. July 14, 1937.

Plate 19.   Development of juvenal Ivory-billed Woodpecker.

Plate 20.   Adult female Ivory-bill skin (left) (M.C.Z. No. 244405) and juvenal Ivory-bill skin
(M.C.Z. No. 242972), both taken near Old Town, Fla., the juvenal bird on April 15, 1892.

CHAPTER 16

Nesting Success and Causes of Nesting Failure

Nesting Success of the Ivory-billed Woodpecker

THE Singer Tract, Louisiana, is the only area where enough observations have been made to warrant drawing any conclusions about the nesting success of the Ivory-bill. The fates of six nests in this tract are known. The histories of three of these have already been described; one young Ivory-bill was raised in each. I examined these nests soon after the young birds had left, and they were all alike in containing nothing but chips and 'sawdust,' fragments of egg shell, a few dried droppings, fragments of feather sheaths, a few small feathers, and some mites. There was nothing to indicate that more than one egg or young had ever been in any of the nests; apparently one egg was laid in each, and one young was successfully raised. It is possible that infertile or broken eggs could have been thrown out, but careful examination of the ground below the nests revealed nothing of this kind, and it is the habit of many if not most birds to leave unhatched eggs in the nest.

The other three nests in the Singer Tract whose fates are known were failures, almost mysteriously destroyed. The histories of the two 1935 nests have been described, where something destroyed the young soon after they had hatched. The third nest had a similar fate (Allen and Kellogg). It was found by J. J. Kuhn on May 13, 1933, located within a hundred yards of the second nest found in 1935. Kuhn visited the nest three times between then and May 27. The birds came to the nest about every eleven to twenty minutes, which indicated that they were feeding young. On June 7, Dr. Frank Oastler came to secure some motion pictures, but when he and Kuhn reached the nest tree, it was deserted. They cut the tree down, and all they found were small fragments of egg shell mixed with chips in the bottom of the cavity.

Broods of young Ivory-bills out of the nest have been seen several times in the Singer Tract, and the following is a summary of those observations:

July 1931, 4 small young seen by J. J. Kuhn
July 1932, 2 young seen by J. J. Kuhn and H. C. Sevier
July 1933, 2 young seen by J. J. Kuhn
May 1936, 4 young seen by J. J. Kuhn and M. Morgan
July 1936, 2 young seen by J. J. Kuhn
March 1937, 1 young
March 1938, 1 young
June 1938, 2 young seen by J. J. Kuhn
April 1939, 1 young.

Since 1931 at least nineteen young in nine broods have been seen in the Singer Tract.

In 1938 and 1939 I made some observations on Pileated Woodpeckers in the Singer Tract to see how their nesting success compared with that of the Ivory-bill. Observations made on the two species are compared in the following table.

COMPARISON OF NESTING SUCCESS AND SIZE OF BROODS OF IVORY-BILLED AND PILEATED WOODPECKERS, SINGER TRACT, MADISON PARISH, LA.

	Ivory-bill (1931–39)	Pileated (1938–39)
Nests observed	6	5
Successful nests	3 (50%)	3 (60%)
Broods observed	9	7
Broods of one young	3 (33%)	2 (28.5%)
Broods of two young	4 (45%)	2 (28.5%)
Broods of three young	0	3 (43%)
Broods of four young	2 (22%)	0

Ivory-bill: 19 young in 9 broods out of nest (2.11/brood).
Pileated: 15 young in 7 broods out of nest (2.14/brood).

There was little difference, considering the few observations that have been made, between the percentage (50%) of successful nests of the Ivory-bill and that (60%) of the Pileated. The average numbers of young in broods observed out of the nest were also approximately the same for the two species (2.11 for the Ivory-bill, 2.14 for the Pileated), but broods of one or two were observed for the Ivory-bill in 78% of the occurrences and for the Pileated in 57%, or, in other words, small numbers of young out of the nest occurred more often in Ivory-bill broods than in Pileated.

The Ivory-bill also lays smaller sets of eggs than do the Southern and Florida Pileated Woodpeckers. The following table compares the number of eggs laid by the two kinds of wood-peckers, from data published and in museums.

COMPARISON OF NUMBER OF EGGS PER SET, IVORY-BILLED
AND PILEATED (SOUTHERN AND FLORIDA) WOODPECKERS

No. of eggs per set	Ivory-bill sets	Pileated sets
2	3	1
3	4	16
4	2	20
5	0	3
Average number of eggs per set	2.9	3.6

It is interesting to compare the nesting success, number of eggs, and numbers of young raised of the Ivory-bill with that of a common species, the Song Sparrow, whose life history has been described in detail by Mrs. M. M. Nice (1937).

COMPARISON OF NESTING SUCCESS OF IVORY-BILLED
WOODPECKER AND SONG SPARROW

	Ivory-bill	Song Sparrow
Nests observed	6	211
Successful nests	3 (50%)	100 (47.4%)
Average number of eggs per nest	2.9	4.1
Average size of broods out of nest	2.1	3.0

Here also, the percentage of nesting success is approximately equal in the two species, and so is the ratio of the average number of young raised to the average number of eggs per nest (2.1/2.9 and 3.0/4.1), but the actual number of eggs and young is smaller for the Ivory-bill. The number of young Song Sparrows raised each year by one pair is further increased by their nesting three or four times in one season; Nice's figures indicate that the average number of young fledged per pair in the entire season is about 4.5.

The important difference between the nesting of the Ivory-bill and other species appears to be that the big woodpecker lays fewer eggs and so raises fewer young. This may be an expression of the general rule that in a group of related birds the larger species usually lay fewer eggs than do the smaller; among the woodpeckers the Downy usually lays four or five, the Hairy four, the Red-bellied four or five, the Pileated three or four, and the Ivory-bill two or three.

The effect that the smaller number has on the existence of the Ivory-bill depends upon survival of the young to breeding age and on the length of the time that an adult can live and successfully breed. There are no data for the Ivory-bill for either of these two subjects, and so there is no way to estimate what the survival ratio of the young is or should be to maintain the species. The figures comparing the breeding success of the Pileated and Ivory-billed Woodpeckers, presented above, indicate that the Pileated is a little more successful and a little more prolific than the Ivory-bill. If it is assumed that these figures hold for the entire population, both past and present, of Ivory-bills and of Pileateds, and also that these two species of woodpeckers have similar survival rates and life spans, the slightly greater reproductive success of the Pileated would in many years result in a cumulative fashion in a considerably greater number of individuals. This hypothesis is open to several objections, the foremost being that it is based on two assumptions, and another being that there is no evidence that there ever was a decreasing number of Ivory-bills in proportion to the number of Pileateds until logging and clearing of land began.

Ivory-bills have nested a second time when their first nest was robbed of eggs. R. D. Hoyt (1905) collected a set of two eggs from a nest in a live cypress near Clermont, Florida, on February 15, 1904; on March 9 he collected a second set of two eggs from the same pair from a nest in a dead cypress seventy-five yards from the first. E. A. McIlhenny describes (Bendire) taking a set of three fresh eggs on April 9, 1892, and on May 19 he took from a nest of the same pair lower down in the same tree a set of four eggs in which incubation was advanced.

One thing has not yet been taken into account in discussing the nesting success of the Ivory-bill, and that is that pairs may not always breed but will go through the season without any attempt at nesting. I strongly suspect that some of the pairs of Ivory-bills seen in the Singer Tract were non-breeding birds, judging from the observations made of their actions by Mr. ·Kuhn and others who saw them and from the fact that they did not seem to be attached to any one area of the tract. Because of the indefiniteness of the observations, it is impossible even to estimate how often mated birds do not breed, or the percentage of non-breeding birds in the population, but it is possible that the greatest factor reducing the rate of reproduction of the Ivory-bill is the failure of some birds to nest. One reason for their not breeding is immaturity, for it is probable that Ivory-bills do not nest until they are at least two years old. Another possibility is that the quantity of food available to the woodpeckers may determine whether they will nest or not. There have been several occurrences recorded (Leopold) when birds have failed to breed under conditions seriously affecting their food supply. Failure to breed may also be caused by lack of synchronization of the reproductive cycles of a mated pair, a subject discussed in later paragraphs.

The numerical strength of the Ivory-bill must be considered when discussing the effects of its breeding habits on the survival of the species. The bird now exists in small isolated groups, such as in the Singer Tract, and as these have diminished in size, it has become more vulnerable to accidental destruction; the chance death of a few individuals could precipitate the extinction of the group.

The usual condition of small broods of the Ivory-bill aggravates the possibility of this happening by preventing numbers of the bird from increasing rapidly and so escaping the risks inseparable from small numbers. The small size of broods coupled with few breeding pairs also decreases the chances of young birds finding mates, by heightening the likelihood of one sex outnumbering the other. Broods of few young probably had little effect on the survival and abundance of the Ivory-bill when it was widespread, but with the few birds now existing, the lower rate of reproduction accentuates the dangers inherent in small numbers.

Discussion of Causes for Nesting Failures

The three nests that were broken up in the Singer Tract, one in 1933 and two in 1935, were all apparently destroyed when they contained young. On examination none showed any signs of blood, albumen, broken eggs, or any indication that predators had taken the nestlings. If a predator was responsible it must have been one that could have reached the nests, which rules out opossums that cannot climb trees the size of the nest trees, and one that could have removed all the young from the nest without spilling any blood or leaving some other mark. It also must have attacked the nest when the adults were away, or else the parent woodpeckers were not able to drive it off. I have seen adult Ivory-bills chase Red-shouldered and Cooper's Hawks away from the nest, and I believe that they would attack other predators.

Raccoons and Barred Owls are the only species that seem capable of attacking a nest under these conditions, and the one most likely to prey on nestling woodpeckers is the Barred Owl. K. A. Wilson found (1938) for one pair of Barred Owls in their breeding season in Michigan that 20% "of their food at this time consisted of birds, mostly woodpeckers." These were undoubtedly smaller species, and a Barred Owl might have trouble carrying off young Ivory-bills, but it is known that they do attack hole-inhabiting birds such as woodpeckers.

The cause for the disappearance of nestlings from these nests is really a mystery. A predator may have been responsible, but there is no definite evidence that that occurred.

When we were watching the Ivory-bill nest in April 1935, we noticed that the adults frequently paused to preen and scratch themselves, sometimes even interrupting their incubating to do this.

Kuhn saw the birds doing much preening when he watched them behaving rather strangely at the nest on April 29. On May 9 this nest was found to be deserted; it was cut down, and Professor Allen preserved the contents of the cavity in a paper bag (Allen and Kellogg). The following morning when we examined the debris it was found to be almost alive with mites. The material was sent to Dr. Arthur Jacot, a specialist on mites, but it reached him in such a dried-out condition that he was able to secure and identify only a small part of what must have originally been in the chips. The list of mites he identified follows (Allen and Kellogg).

Oribatidae—eaters of wood, fungi and algae
  1—*Galumna*
  1—*Carabodes*
  1—*Platynothrus*
  1—*Suctobelba*
Predaceous
  1—*Chelytus*
  1—*Uropodid*
  1—*Gamasid*
Parasitic?
  3—of the group Anachotricha family?

The other deserted nest that was examined in 1935 had no signs of mites, and those birds did not appear to scratch and preen themselves as much as the first pair had done. Dr. Frank Oastler and Mr. Kuhn did not notice any mites in the deserted nest they examined in 1933.

In 1938 I removed some of the debris from the bottom of the Ivory-bill nest just after the young had left and sent it to Dr. Jacot for determination of its fauna. In a letter dated April 2, 1938, he wrote:

The mites from the Ivory-bills' nest included:
2 feather mites (parasitic on feathers), several immature Chelytids—predaceous, 3 species of Parasitidae—predaceous. Thus the fauna of this nest was quite different from that of the former. It has the aspect of being newer and of having such an abundance of predaceous mites that other mites, etc., must have been well under control.

A second letter from him stated that the material from this nest also contained several flea larvae, which could affect the birds only as adult fleas.

Parasitic mites were apparently more abundant in the first 1935 nest than in any other examined. To quote A. A. Allen and P. P. Kellogg (1937) remarking on this nest:

Knowing from experience of mites having killed young House Wrens, Redstarts, Louisiana Water-thrushes, Phoebes, and other birds, we wondered if they could not have been responsible for the destruction of the young Ivory-bills, either by killing the young outright or by causing so much nervousness on the part of the parents that the eggs failed to hatch or the young be properly brooded. The small fragments of egg-shells left in the nest favor the belief that the young hatched as the shell fragments were about the size that one normally finds in a woodpecker's nest after the larger pieces have been carried away by the parent birds. What became of the dead young remains a mystery, though with some birds it is common practice to remove dead young from the nest if they die during the period that they are being brooded. We have known

Flickers to leave one or more dead in the bottom of the hole while they continued to feed the others, but in such cases the young were so large they were no longer being brooded and the parents doubtless did not know what had occurred . . . many young birds of other species manage to survive even when heavily infested with mites.

In each of these three incidents, the adult Ivory-bills were not to be found in the vicinity of the nest after they had abandoned it. There was not enough evidence found around any of the nests to determine the cause for the destruction and disappearance of the nestlings; parasitic mites may have been a factor in one nest, but the evidence is not clear, and the other two apparently were destroyed in some entirely different manner.

Because of the scarcity of Ivory-bills, they may occasionally inbreed, birds of the same parentage pairing, and that has been suggested as a possible cause for nest failure in the Ivory-bill; inbreeding among some domesticated animals results in poor reproduction and weak young. But the evidence is that among wild birds and mammals inbreeding causes no ill effects. L. O. Shelley (1932 and 1935) reports that a female Downy Woodpecker, raised in 1930, mated in 1931 with her own brother of the same brood, and that year they successfully raised four young. They nested in the same vicinity for four seasons, each time successfully, in 1934 raising a brood of five young. M. M. Nice (1937) describes a brother and sister pair of Song Sparrows that mated when a year old, and successfully hatched three eggs. Aldo Leopold (1933) cites the extreme productivity of the inbred population of rabbits in Australia. I believe that there is no valid reason for suspecting that inbreeding, if it has occurred, has harmfully affected the Ivory-bill.

The production of infertile eggs is another possible cause for a low rate of reproduction. A set of three eggs reported to have been collected from an Ivory-bill nest in Pumpkin swamp, Lafayette (now Dixie) County, Florida, on April 19, 1893 (Wayne, 1910, and field catalogue), had a large embryo in one while the other two eggs were addled. This set, from the Ralph Sutton Collection, is now in the U. S. National Museum (Current No. 26365), where I have seen it. The eggs are very small, smaller than many Pileated Woodpecker eggs, and if they were laid by an Ivory-bill, they must have been laid by a young female, as young birds regularly if not always lay smaller eggs than do old birds. Wayne's field catalogue lists a female Ivory-bill specimen collected from this locality nine days after the set was secured, but I did not find the specimen in any of the museum collections I examined, so had no other evidence to judge the age of the bird that might have laid the set. The addled condition of the two eggs might well be correlated with their small size and the probability that they were laid by a young female. There is no other record of infertile or addled eggs being found in Ivory-bill nests. They could be recognized, of course, only in sets that had been considerably incubated; the only records for such sets are by Hoyt (1905) and McIlhenny (Bendire), who described clutches of two and four eggs, respectively, in which incubation was advanced, but neither author happened to mention the presence of sterile or addled eggs.

Allen and Kellogg (1937) have suggested that difference in sex rhythm between paired Ivory-bills might affect their nesting success. This could be especially important in birds as scarce as the Ivory-bill, as they would be handicapped in finding a mate with synchronized reproductive or fertility cycles. Lack of synchronization of the sex cycles apparently occurs in some species and results in infertile eggs. The only case on record of Ivory-bills having had infertile eggs has just been discussed.

In the preceding section it was mentioned that pairs of Ivory-bills occasionally may not breed, and differences in the cycles of a mated pair may be one of the causes for this. Although this is only hypothetical, it would be much more likely to happen in species like the Ivory-bill with an irregular breeding season than it would in more normal birds.

CHAPTER 17

Summary of the Reproductive Habits of the Ivory-billed Woodpecker

IVORY-BILLED Woodpeckers breed at varying times from January to May. The number of eggs laid in a set usually varies from one to four, averaging 2.9. The numbers of eggs and young have been smaller, one or two, in nests begun in January or February, than the number, three or four, in nests begun in April or May.

Ivory-bill nests are excavated in living or dead trees usually about forty to sixty feet from the ground. In Florida they have preferred cypress, but in Louisiana they have nested in a variety of hardwoods. The nest entrance usually measures $4^1/_2$ inches wide by $5^1/_4$ inches from top to bottom. The cavity is generally about nineteen inches deep.

Eggs are incubated about twenty days. The male bird stays in the nest overnight, and during the day the pair alternates on the nest.

Young birds probably stay in the nest five weeks. They are fed regularly by both parents, usually from thirty times a day at first, to fifteen times a day just before nest leaving. The male parent broods overnight and does most of the brooding in the daytime. The male cleans the nest.

Young birds out of the nest follow their parents on feeding trips and are fed by the adults for two months or longer. During a period of between two and three months out of the nest they can find food regularly for themselves and soon afterward can become independent. They usually separate from their parents by winter, but the time for this happening varies.

Three out of six Ivory-bill nests were successful. The size of broods observed out of the nest has averaged 2.11, but broods of one or two have occurred 78% of the time. The percent of nesting success and the ratio of average size of successful broods to average size of egg sets approximately equal those figures for the Pileated Woodpecker and the Song Sparrow, but the Ivory-bill lays fewer eggs and so rears fewer young. Ivory-bills will, sometimes at least, nest a second time if the first nest with eggs is broken up. The rate of reproduction for the Ivory-bill may be lowered by the occurrence of non-breeding birds.

No definite causes for the failure of Ivory-bill nests have been found, although several have been discussed.

Part V.   Conservation of the Ivory-billed Woodpecker

CHAPTER 18

Requirements and General Policy of a Conservation Program

IVORY-BILLED Woodpeckers have become almost extinct because of destruction of their habitat. They lived in the swamp forests of the southeastern coastal plain and the lower Mississippi River, where their home was among the oak, gum, and other big trees in those swamps. Settlement and civilization carried the axe and saw into the forests, and as the trees were cut and the forests destroyed, the Ivory-bills disappeared from region after region, from swamp after swamp.

The real reason for the Ivory-bills' disappearance, as the forests were logged, is apparently this: cutting the big trees of the virgin forests destroyed the woodpeckers' food supply. This happened because certain conditions usually found only in these kinds of forests were changed.

Virgin or primitive forests contain many old trees which, because of their age, are gradually and constantly weakening and dying. Dead limbs and branches and standing trunks of dead trees are abundantly present in all stages of decay, from hard wood with the bark still tight to wood that is punky and completely rotten. This condition is probably more common in the swamp forests of the southeastern states than elsewhere, for there the warmth and great moisture allow rapid growth of trees to a large size, hastening their maturity and their decline, and also speeding the process of decay. This abundance and variety of dead wood present ideal conditions for the development of wood-boring insect larvae, which are the food of woodpeckers, and several kinds of woodpeckers are found commonly in these virgin forests, probably being more abundant there than anywhere else in North America.

The number of wood-boring larvae inhabiting the great amount of dead wood is the reason not only for the abundance of ordinary woodpeckers, but also for the presence of Ivory-bills in some of these forests. Ivory-bills feed mainly upon the kinds of borers (larvae of Buprestid and Ceramby-cid beetles) that bore or mine between the bark and sapwood of dead limbs and trees. These larvae are very abundant when found, but they are present for only a comparatively short time. They are the first to appear in a tree or limb that has died, usually about a year after death; they are commonest under the bark of wood that has been dead about two years, and then they quickly disappear. Because of its short existence in one place, the food of Ivory-bills is relatively scarce and very irregularly distributed in the forest. An Ivory-bill can find food only in some dead trees or parts of trees, and once these have passed a certain stage of decay, the Ivory-bill can no longer secure food there.

Other kinds of woodpeckers eat borers that mine deep in the decaying sapwood and heartwood of dead trees for from two to ten years after the death of the wood, a much longer period. Therefore, their food is much more common and widespread, and they can live in many kinds of forests. On the other hand, Ivory-bills must live where numbers of trees are constantly dying, so that they can find enough trees or limbs with borers beneath the bark.

Logging the virgin forests removes most of the large, old trees which, indirectly, supply food to woodpeckers. Young trees spring up to take the empty places; but young trees grow rapidly, are healthy, and usually contain little dead wood. For woodpeckers they are not much good. Second-growth forests support far fewer woodpeckers than do primeval forests; for example, in the virgin timber of the Singer Tract, Louisiana, the population of Pileated Woodpeckers was from three to six pairs per square mile, but in the neighboring second growth there was less than one pair per square mile. Even in the warm swamps a tree will grow for about 150 years before it is 'old,' so it would take many years of uninterrupted growth for a forest once logged to become again ideal habitat for woodpeckers. In the meantime, these birds would greatly decrease or disappear.

Because of their food habits, Ivory-billed Woodpeckers are more endangered by the cutting of old trees than are other species of woodpeckers. Other kinds can find food in trees in all stages of decay, so their food is much more widespread, and they are able to live in many places where Ivory-bills cannot. Ivory-bills, on the other hand, can find enough food only in places where dead and dying trees are common, which is usually only in old, virgin forests.

There is further evidence that food is the decisive or 'limiting' factor for Ivory-billed Woodpeckers. Several times in various parts of Florida many trees have been killed by fire, storms, or other causes. Ivory-bills have appeared in these places and fed upon these trees as long as the borers beneath the bark were common, and then they have disappeared, moved elsewhere. In the Singer Tract in Louisiana, the same thing has happened: Ivory-bills lived in a territory where their food was temporarily abundant and later departed. From other parts of the Singer Tract where Ivory-bills had lived for a long time the birds disappeared without apparent reason, but research I carried out indicated that their disappearance was also caused by a decrease in the amount of woodpecker food. This subject of the Ivory-bills' food supply is discussed more completely in the chapter of this report on 'The Effect of Quantity of Food on the Distribution of the Ivory-billed Woodpecker.'

Other possible causes for the near extinction of Ivory-billed Woodpeckers were studied, but none were found that ranked in importance with the destruction of its habitat and food supply. Ivory-bills were apparently rarely affected by predators or by competition with any other species. There has never been any indication of disease or parasites. Shooting by man has killed many Ivory-bills, but only from very few localities has this driven out or exterminated the bird. This is a danger, however, that increases as the number of Ivory-bills decreases. Since the motive for shooting the birds has been the curiosity of casual hunters as frequently as it has been the desire of

collectors for securing specimens, control of this danger depends on the exclusion of all hunters from Ivory-bill localities.

When this Ivory-bill research first began, it was thought that the secret of the species' disappearance would be found in some fault or failure of its reproductive habits. The only conclusion that can be drawn, however, from a study of its reproduction, is that the breeding potential or rate of reproduction is naturally low, as it is with many large birds. The number of eggs laid in a set varies from one to four, with the average being 2.9. The average number of young in broods that have been observed out of the nest is 2.1. Broods of only one or two young have been observed frequently, about 78% of the time. The rate is low and probably always has been. When the Ivory-bills were widespread, this naturally low rate of reproduction probably made little if any difference, since there seemed to be few predators or other causes of natural death. But today with the species on the verge of extinction, it complicates the problem of its conservation by slowing the rate of increase and prolonging the risk due to the scarcity of the species.

If we are to preserve the Ivory-billed Woodpecker from extinction, we must maintain for the remaining birds and their offspring a habitat that will supply them with food. This will be the most important requirement, for destruction of the food supply of the Ivory-bill has been the main cause of its disappearance, and the amount of food has often been the factor controlling the existence of the birds. We must take definite steps to preserve and maintain a proper habitat, for otherwise the birds will disappear.

It is probable that in the near future many of the forests in the southeastern states will either be gone or will be managed by foresters for a timber supply. In such a forest, dead and dying trees would be removed, old trees cut to make way for young and growing trees, fires prevented, and all possible steps would be taken to increase the yield of timber. Such methods would harm all woodpeckers, which thrive where dead wood and old trees are abundant, and they would mean starvation for the Ivory-bills, which would not have enough food in a forest managed strictly for its timber supply. Consequently, there is little or no possibility of Ivory-billed Woodpeckers ever again becoming widespread, nor of even continuing to exist unless definite steps are taken to save them.

In forming a general policy for the conservation of the Ivory-billed Woodpecker, two main facts are important. One of these has just been discussed, the necessity of keeping a habitat which can supply enough food for the birds. The second follows: at present the only suitable habitat for the Ivory-bills is in tracts or areas of virgin timber, and these forests are also the home of many other kinds of wild birds and animals, some of them also in need of protection and conservation. Preservation of these forests would not only secure a habitat for the Ivory-bill, it would also save and protect other species. More than that, the entire area with all its life, plant and animal, would be a primitive or wilderness area, an example in perpetuity of the North American wilderness. That is where the Ivory-bill fits; a denizen of the tall trees in thick forests and swamps, he belongs in the same place as Wild Turkeys, bear, alligators, and other residents of our southern swamp wilderness. The most will be accomplished by preserving an area of virgin and primitive forest that will be a suitable habitat for the Ivory-billed Woodpecker and other forms of life, the whole a permanent monument of native trees, plants, birds and other animals inhabiting that wilderness area.

Some conservationists have expressed the fear that Ivory-billed Woodpeckers are now so few that no program of conservation could prevent them from becoming extinct. It is true that a species low in numbers is exposed to many dangers, that there may be difficulties in individuals finding proper mates, and other complications. But I do not believe that in the case of the Ivory-bill the scarcity of the species is such an important factor as it might be in others. Ivory-bills are not social or gregarious birds; they have apparently always lived in solitary pairs, and as long as the birds can mate, they are capable of reproduction and increase. With small numbers, inbreeding could occur, but there is no evidence that this would be harmful. Large numbers are not necessary for the continued existence of the Ivory-bill. Even though it would be better and more promising if the birds were more abundant, still they are not, and if we are to make any attempt to save the species, we must be satisfied in starting with a few individuals.

The following chapters describe first the four important Ivory-bill localities, their locations, general characteristics, and the facts known about Ivory-bills in each, and next the specific measures that should or could be accomplished in any area set aside for the conservation of Ivory-billed Woodpeckers.

CHAPTER 19

Principal Ivory-billed Woodpecker Localities

THE Singer Tract, located in Madison Parish, Louisiana, is the most important and best known of the remaining Ivory-bill habitats. Originally it was a tract of 81,000 acres, four-fifths of it being virgin bottomland forest of sweet gum, oak, ash, elm, and other trees. Logging rights on parts of the tract were sold by the Singer Sewing Machine Company to the Tendal Lumber Company and the Chicago Mill and Lumber Company in the years 1937 and 1939. Logging of the tract began in 1937 and at the time of my last trip there, December 1941, about 40% of the tract had been cut over. Most of the best parts of the tract, fortunately, had not yet been reached, but some had been partly cut and all is in danger.

In the spring of 1939, the last season of the Ivory-bill research project, there were one pair and their one young of that year, and three other solitary, unmated birds, making a total of six individuals in the Singer Tract. On a short trip to the tract in December of 1941, I found that the number of Ivory-bills apparently had not changed.

The logging that was going on in the tract at that time threatened the habitat of the remaining Ivory-bills. It was once hoped that the Singer Tract would be preserved in its entirety and wildness for all time, but that is no longer possible. Selected parts of the tract may still be preserved, or the logging may be done in a way that will least affect the woodpeckers; those are about the only alternatives left. A description of the possible ways of logging that will least harm the Ivory-bills' habitat is described in the following chapter, 'Specific Measures for the Conservation of the Ivory-billed Woodpecker.'

Certain parts of the tract are much better habitat for Ivory-bills than others. Food seems to be more available in them, the woodpeckers nest and do most of their feeding there. The map, Fig. 22, shows the location of these areas; sections shaded on the map are the absolute minimum worth preserving. It would be far preferable to make the regions larger; sections enclosed with the heavy dashed line are the best areas for addi-tions to the minimum areas, but, of course, even larger areas would be better.

The following is a list of sections, or parts of sections, their numbers, townships, and ranges, which contain the best habitat for Ivory-bills:

Sections 60 and 61, in T16N, R12E.
Northern halves of sections 12 and 13, in T15N, R12E.

The above sections are in what is called the John's Bayou area. Additions to this minimum area should be made on the west and north for from a half mile to a mile of the boundary of the minimum area.

Sections 24, 25, and the eastern half of 26, T15N, R11E.

These are in what is called the Mack's Bayou area. Additions to the minimum area should be made on the west and south for a half mile from the boundary of the above named sections.

The minimum areas recommended above are the best for the preservation of Ivory-bills, and the areas recommended for addition are next best. Further enlargement would be desirable if possible, because they would make that much more habitat for the birds.

The Singer Tract is important for the conservation of other forms of wildlife as well as the Ivory-bill. It is unique in that every form of animal native to the region, except those extinct, is still living there. Deer and Wild Turkey are abundant; wolves, including black individuals, bear, and panther are present; big alligators still swim in the lakes; and smaller animals and birds are everywhere abundant. The richness of the plant life is another reason for its preservation. Big trees of several species stand throughout the forest and make it a beautiful place (Plate 4). This forest affords an excellent example, and is the last remaining large stand, of the primeval forest that once covered all the bottomlands of the Mississippi Delta.

The Singer Tract, before so much of it was logged, would have made an excellent national park or monument of North American wilderness.

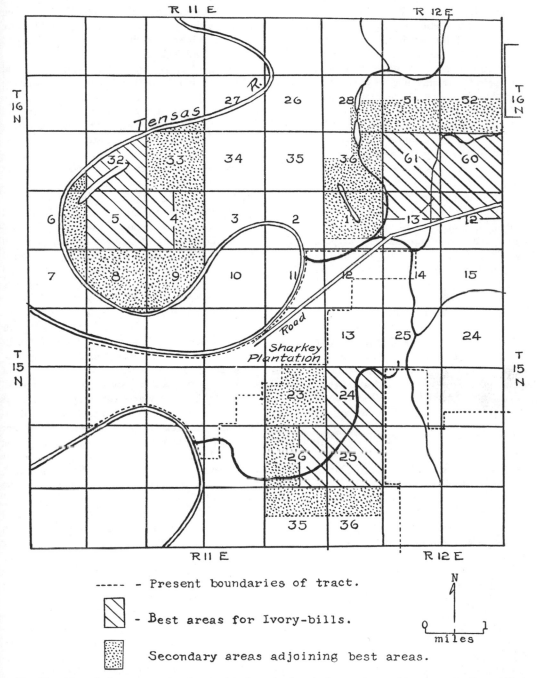

Fig. 22.   Map of Singer Tract, Madison Parish, La., showing the best and second-best areas for Ivory-billed Woodpeckers.

91

Logging already done has destroyed much of value, but there still is territory worth saving. At the time of this writing (April 1942), the demands of a war-geared nation make it very difficult to obtain money or governmental action on such project. It may not, however, be too late for the saving of some of the tract. To accomplish that will be worth much effort.

The Big Cypress region, mostly in Collier and partly in Hendry Counties, Florida (see map, Fig. 14), is probably the second most important region for the conservation of the Ivory-billed Woodpecker. There the land is very flat, mostly covered with scattered pine woods, grass, and low palmettoes, and running across this flat land are the long lines or 'strands' of semitropical cypress swamp that make up the Big Cypress. The larger strands are from ten to twenty-five miles long, and from one-half to four miles wide. In the swamps the vegetation is thick and tangled, with cypress the commonest and biggest tree standing and with many semitropical trees such as royal palm, strangler fig, and pond apple.

During my field work in the Big Cypress region, which lasted a little more than a month, I did not actually find any Ivory-bills, but I investigated several reports and inspected much of the country. Two or more of the reports seemed authentic and reliable. The swamps where the birds were reported seen were remote and untouched, and were near localities where Ivory-bills had been collected several years before. Judging from these facts, it is probable that some of the woodpeckers still exist there, in one of the wildest regions of all Florida. From the location of the reports and the size of the swamps, I estimated that there were probably about six individuals present, but there could be more or less.

The largest swamp in the region, and the one most likely to have Ivory-bills, is called the Thickahatchie or Fakahatchie swamp. It is from two to four miles wide and extends at least twenty miles. The vegetation there is more tropical than in other parts of the Big Cypress, and partly because it is hard to enter and partly because some of it is included in a state game-breeding area, wildlife is more abundant there than in most other parts of the Big Cypress. Another locality where

Ivory-bills were reported seen was East Crossing at the southern end of the Main Strand. Here the swamp is smaller, but it is remote, hard to reach, and still primitive.

The Big Cypress is the home of many birds and animals. Ibises, herons, and other water birds are abundant in the swamps; bear and panther live along the edges of the strands; and deer and turkey are still common where they have not been hunted too steadily. It is a naturalist's paradise, much of it little known. Birds and animals are everywhere, and the beauty of open spaces and pine woods contrasts with the luxuriant swamp vegetation growing in almost tropical density.

Of all the wilderness areas in the eastern United States, this cypress region is the most primitive. Very little of it has been changed by man, and with the exception of paroquets and wolves, its original animal life is apparently intact. For these and other reasons, it is superbly worthy of being preserved as a primitive or wilderness area. It would take more investigation, to be sure, of the best parts, but I would place the Thickahatchie or Fakahatchie swamp first, and the lower or southern end of the Main Strand second. The proposed Everglades National Park includes none of the real cypress, which it should if it ever materializes, for the Big Cypress is far superior in plant and animal life to most of the area at present included in the proposed park. It will take further investigation there before the real status of the Ivory-bills can be found; that will be a difficult task because of the great area, difficulty of travel, and because so little is known about much of the Big Cypress.

Efforts should be made to save this unusual region from exploitation before it is too late. Even though we know less about Ivory-bills in the Big Cypress than we do in the Singer Tract, the former is so much more primitive that it is quite possible it will be the region where Ivory-bills will make their last stand.

The Apalachicola River swamp in northwestern Florida contains good habitat for Ivory-bills, and although none have been seen by recognized naturalists, natives and hunters have described birds resembling them, and I found some woodpecker work which resembled the work of

Ivory-bills. The Apalachicola swamp is a large alluvial or bottomland swamp, the best being about thirty miles long and five miles wide. Much of the lower part of the swamp is a forest of tupelo gum, not good for Ivory-bills, but along the west of Brothers River (see map, Fig. 16) is the Willis swamp which was virgin forest in 1939 and contained good habitat for the birds. It was from that region that most of the reports of Ivory-bills came, and in there I found what appeared to be Ivory-bill sign. Farther upriver, along the Florida River, is the Ben May Tract which was virgin timber in 1939, and although I could find no reports or signs of Ivory-bills being in that area, it is suitable for them and is another possible habitat.

In 1939, when I investigated the Apalachicola swamp, I estimated from the size of the forest and the locations of the reports of Ivory-bills, that there probably were two pairs or four individuals in the lower part of the swamp. I was not able to learn much on my visit because of the season, June, and the lack of a boat and motor necessary for efficient travel in that swamp.

The lower part of the Apalachicola never has been thoroughly investigated by competent naturalists. It should be because it has good possibilities as a wildlife and wilderness area, and because we need to know more about the Ivory-billed Woodpecker there. Although not as wild, primitive, and unusual as either the Singer Tract or the Big Cypress, it is still inhabited by bear and other game animals, and is one of the largest river swamps in the country, with some parts of it almost untouched by logging.

The Santee River in South Carolina is another large river bordered by a big bottomland swamp. Ivory-bills were definitely seen there several times prior to 1938, but as far as I know none have been seen since. Most of the Ivory-bill records were in the Wadmacaun Island section near the lower end of the river (see map, Fig. 13), but thorough search there after the fall of 1937 failed to find any birds or signs of them in that region. Other reports came from Black Oak Island; the timber there was excellent habitat for Ivory-bills, and I found some likely looking sign there in 1939, but

nothing any more definite to prove their presence.

Since 1939 the Black Oak Island section has been cut over, a dam built across the river there, and most of the island and forest flooded to make a reservoir for the Santee-Cooper power project. This permanently destroyed that Ivory-bill habitat, but for one possibility. All the trees in the flooded area were not cut, and if any of these drowned trees will stand above the water, the dead tops and trunks might for some time supply food to Ivory-bills and other woodpeckers and attract them into that area.

In 1939 there was some virgin timber around Wee Tee Lake, but that was being cut. The best place for Ivory-bills to survive after the completion of the power project and the logging just mentioned will be again in the Wadmacaun Island region. On that island there is quite an area of virgin timber, probably the best remaining tract in the southeast of Cypress River swamp, with some oak and gum, the whole worthy of being preserved as an example of that almost vanished type of primeval forest.

It is desirable, because of the facts just described, that an interest and a watch be kept in the Santee region. Ivory-bills may well find an abundant food supply among the drowned trees of the Santee reservoir for a year or so, and then move down river to Wadmacaun Island, providing the fine forest there is not logged.

The four areas described above—the Singer Tract in Louisiana, the Big Cypress and Apalachicola River swamp in Florida, and the Santee swamp in South Carolina—are the best possibilities as refuges for the Ivory-billed Woodpecker. Ivory-bills are probably still present in the region extending from Gulf Hammock, Levy County, to Bear Bay, Dixie County, Florida (see map, Fig. 15), but there is no one region there where they are known to live. The birds apparently are scattered and wandering, so there is no place that would be suitable as a preserve. The whole region is wild and quite sparsely settled, frequently exposed to fires and storms which kill timber, and it is possible that some birds may live there for a long time without special protection.

CHAPTER 20

Specific Measures for the Conservation of the Ivory-billed Woodpecker

Area Required for an Ivory-bill Refuge

ONE of the first problems to meet in planning a refuge for Ivory-billed Woodpeckers would be the area of forest necessary. Studies of the Ivory-bills in the Singer Tract indicate that the minimum area for one pair of the birds should be two and a half to three square miles. They do not need all of that forest at any one time, but that much would be necessary to insure an adequate food supply from year to year. In other regions the required area would probably be the same size, providing the forest were just as suitable. More forest would, of course, be required if it were not as good for the birds. Suitability of a forest can be roughly judged by the abundance of other species of woodpeckers; in portions of the Singer Tract inhabited by Ivory-bills, there were five or six pairs of Pileated Woodpeckers per square mile, and that figure can probably be used as a guide to the adequacy of a forest.

A minimum area of two to three square miles would allow room for one pair of Ivory-bills; more would be required for other pairs and for their offspring to find breeding territory. The larger the forest the better for the conservation of the birds—that is certain.

Other considerations in deciding the size of an area to be chosen as an Ivory-bill refuge are the preservation of forest types, some of which may not be useful for Ivory-bills but might well be included in the same protected area, the conservation of forms of wildlife which might require a different type of habitat, and the inclusion of any other desirable features.

Selective Logging in an Ivory-bill Refuge

The greatest obstacle to the establishment of refuges for Ivory-billed Woodpeckers has been the high cost of the areas. The only suitable regions are virgin forests where the timber possesses a high market value. The price of cypress and swamp hardwood timber has risen rapidly in recent years and is still rising as the stands of this type of timber dwindle to the end.

Since high cost is the chief obstacle, suitable tracts could be more easily acquired if the cost could be lowered; one possible way of doing this would be by a plan of selective logging to obtain some return from the sale of timber while still preserving the suitability of the forest for Ivory-bills. Such a plan has the following four objectives: (1) to preserve the suitability of the forest for Ivory-bills; (2) to protect habitats for wildlife such as deer, turkey, bear, alligator, and many others; (3) to preserve good examples of different types of virgin forest; (4) to secure as high a yield from the timber as possible while still accomplishing the other objectives.

If such a program is to be tried in a tract established as an Ivory-billed Woodpecker refuge, the first step would be division of the tract into three kinds of areas, as follows:

Reserve areas—the best Ivory-bill habitats, range for other birds and animals, and examples of virgin timber; not to be logged but to be left as primitive forest.

Partial cutting areas—Ivory-bill feeding range of secondary importance; to be selectively cut.

Logging areas—poorest areas from all standpoints; to be logged.

The map of the Singer Tract, Fig. 22, shows how that tract could be divided into the three kinds of areas. The shaded parts would be 'reserve areas,' where there is the best Ivory-bill habitat; the parts next to these, enclosed by the heavy dashed line, could be 'partial cutting areas'; and the rest could be in 'logging areas.' The amount included in each kind of area would depend in part on how much return would be necessary from the cutting of timber and, of course, could be varied considerably from the suggestions outlined above for the Singer Tract, especially in the direction of enlarging the reserve areas at the expense of others.

The reserve areas are to be left untouched and would constitute the nuclei of the refuge. Parts of the tract which are known to be inhabited regularly by Ivory-bills should be included, and so

94

should certain sections of the forest valuable as examples of primitive forest or as wildlife habitat.

The partial cutting areas are to be selectively logged, but not in the manner that the term 'selective logging' usually implies. The selective logging of good forestry practice is designed to increase the yield from the forest by removing the older and slow-growing trees to allow more room, moisture, and light to young, rapidly growing trees; it is generally designed to produce a sustained yield. Such a practice would remove the very trees upon which the Ivory-bill depends for food. The aim in the partial cutting areas should be to remove the greatest value of merchantable timber without harming the Ivory-bill habitat. All trees supplying or likely to supply any appreciable quantity of food to Ivory-bills are to be left standing, and only sound, healthy trees are to be cut. The graph of Fig. 20 and the table in the section treating the food habits of the Ivory-bill show that the species of trees fed upon most frequently by the birds, at least in the Singer Tract, are sweet gum, Nuttall's oak, and hackberry. The chief complication in planning the logging on the partial cutting areas is that sweet gum, upon which the Ivory-bills feed more than any other tree, has the highest market value as timber. This will be partly compensated for by the fact that trees which can supply food to woodpeckers are usually unsound, containing rotten or defective logs, and will not yield the volume that will the healthy, sound trees.

The exact percentage or volume of trees to be removed in partial cutting areas depends on the policy to be followed in managing the tract. An attempt can be made to cut on a more or less sustained yield basis, handling the area to supply continually both woodpecker feeding trees and timber, or the area can be cut to obtain the highest immediate monetary return in order to reduce the cost of acquiring the tract. The first policy would almost certainly be more profitable.

The treatment of each tree in the partial logging areas depends on what kind of a tree it is and on its condition, which determine its importance for woodpecker feeding and its value as timber. All trees of any species that are mostly dead should be left, and so should trees where there is a good possibility of their being defective, yielding cull logs; trees that are mostly dead or are defective in some way usually yield few sound logs, and more is to be gained by leaving them standing. The following is an outline of the qualities of the trees that are important Ivory-bill feeding trees in the Singer Tract, Louisiana, and the suggested treatment for each kind in partial cutting areas. Similar conditions will be found in other bottomland forests, but an area like the Big Cypress in Florida would require different measures.

Sweet gum—the most important and valuable timber species in the tract, but the one most frequently used by the Ivory-bill; to be cut only when sound, usable logs can be secured, leaving all trees that have tops one-third or more dead.

Nuttall's oak—value of timber fairly high, but used frequently by the Ivory-bill; also produces many big acorns for deer and turkey; to be cut sparingly and only when sound logs can be obtained.

Hackberry—not valuable as timber; to be left standing.

Trees of some importance to the Ivory-bill and of low value as timber: overcup oak, American elm, cedar elm, red maple, water hickory, pecan, and honey locust—only trees yielding sound, clear logs to be cut, the majority to be left standing.

Trees not important to the Ivory-bill and of moderate to fairly high value as timber: cypress, willow oak, water oak, persimmon, and green ash—all to be cut except, as noted in preceding paragraph, those that are noticeably defective or mostly dead.

Any forest within the refuge area that is very poor for Ivory-bill feeding ground or for other purposes may be placed in logging areas. These areas are to be cut over for the largest possible return from the timber, or can be managed on a sustained-yield basis, depending on the policy to be pursued in the management of the tract and on the recommendations of a competent forester familiar with conditions in the local region.

In the partial cutting areas, trees to be cut will have to be marked before operations begin, and success of the program will depend largely upon the skill with which trees are selected. A sufficient number of old and dead-topped trees must be left to maintain a feeding ground for the Ivory-bill. No rules can be laid down for the selection of trees for cutting beyond those guides already described; each tree must be judged on its own condition as to whether it is more valuable as a feeding tree for woodpeckers or as timber. The closeness of the cutting of trees will also depend on how much monetary return from the logging operations is desired. The only means of estimating how much timber the partial cutting areas can be expected to yield is by a timber cruise.

Logging operations should be done by truck and tractor, since that method damages the woods less than does building a tramline and, being more flexible, is better suited to the conditions of selective logging. The best seasons for logging in this manner are summer and fall when the ground is dry, and they would also be the best times for operations in the tract as there would be no possibility of disturbing breeding birds. The logging can probably be done by private contracting parties under supervision of the administration of the refuge.

Artificial Increase of the Woodpecker Food Supply

The amount of woodpecker food can be artificially increased by girdling or otherwise killing trees. Audubon wrote (1842) that Ivory-bills were "sometimes observed working upon and chipping off the bark from the belted trees of newly cleared plantations." W. E. D. Scott (1898) once saw eleven Ivory-bills in Florida feeding together on some girdled timber near a cypress swamp. A farmer living close to the Singer Tract told me that he had seen a pair of the birds come to some 'new ground,' which he had cleared, to feed on the trees killed by poisoning. These records show that the Ivory-bill can and will feed on trees killed by man, and that the amount of food for the bird can be increased in this way, but a little experimenting needs to be done in order to find the best ways of killing trees so that they will support large numbers of borers. I have killed trees by fire and by girdling, chopping a complete ring around the trees into the sapwood, both methods being successful at least part of the time in creating dead trees with many borers in them; at other times I have girdled trees that died so slowly that they were just beginning to be attacked by insects two years after the girdling. Poisoning by sodium arsenate is practiced frequently in deadening trees on land cleared for cultivation. The poison probably makes trees a little less suitable for insects, for I have examined several poisoned trees that had no signs of having harbored borers.

Deadening trees for the woodpeckers can be done so as to improve the timber stand at the same time, by killing defective or undesirable individuals. Trees that are crooked or with many limbs, or that are of some undesirable species like cedar elm that has low quality timber and little value for wildlife, trees that overtop and repress more desirable individuals, or are in crowded groups that need thinning, all of these can be killed to increase the supply of woodpecker food and at the same time improve the stand for all wildlife and for the quality of timber.

Increasing the woodpecker food supply by artificially killing trees is still very much in the experimental stage. At the outset of such operations, several ways of deadening trees should be tried—poisoning, building fires at the base, using a blowtorch to kill a ring around the trunk by heat, and by any other reasonable means. These experiments should be planned so that the effects of using different methods can be observed easily and without ambiguity. Killing trees in one plot by one method, in another by a second, and so on, repeating the plots, and then comparing the plots as to the approximate abundance of borers and the amount of feeding done in each by the Ivory-bill and other woodpeckers will determine most quickly the effective methods.

Many biologists and others interested in the conservation of the Ivory-bills have wondered if the birds could find food in the dead tree tops and other waste left after a logging operation. Occasionally the woodpeckers have been seen feeding on such slash, but mostly they have not, even when much of it was available. There are several apparent reasons for this. The first is that the dead limbs and branches left after logging rarely have borers living beneath the bark, the kind that Ivory-bills hunt. I have examined several cutover areas and found this to be true. Perhaps it is because the fallen wood partly in contact with the soil rots too quickly, or there may be so much wood killed at one time that there are not enough wood-boring insects even to begin to lay eggs in all the limbs and branches; or it may be a combination of the two, as most of these insects have life cycles lasting a year or more, so the wood decays before they can multiply enough to fill the dead tops with larvae. Unless most of the slash contains borers, a woodpecker does not hunt through all for the few limbs that do. Whatever the reason, little woodpecker food seems to be present in the fallen material.

Another reason for Ivory-bills not feeding much in places like this is that they usually avoid coming near the ground. The only times they have been observed near or on the ground were when they had fed gradually down a standing tree trunk. Frequently in the forest I have seen fallen tree trunks full of the borers that the Ivory-bill prefers, but never have I seen one of the birds feeding on such a trunk.

If scarcity of the insects is the reason for the lack of Ivory-bills feeding on the slash, that perhaps can be remedied by logging slowly and allowing time for the insect population to increase so that they can fill the available dead wood. Except for this, there is little possibility of Ivory-bills securing food from this source.

Protection of Ivory-billed Woodpeckers

Any refuge where Ivory-bills are to be protected should be patrolled by efficient wardens to keep out all hunters of any kind. Where there are only a few birds in an isolated area, those few must be completely protected to insure their continued existence, for the loss of one or two individuals may be the beginning of the end. Experience in the Singer Tract has shown that *all* hunters must be barred. The seemingly innate desire of most hunters to kill and examine a spectacular bird is a constant threat.

Laws prohibiting hunting on a refuge are not enough; it must be protected by good wardens who are willing to work persistently at the arduous, often thankless, and sometimes dangerous job of keeping out poachers. Visitors to the refuge should be required to have permits to enter, to aid the wardens in checking up on persons within the area.

Trapping and Moving Ivory-bills to Other Areas

If any Ivory-bill habitat is going to be destroyed, as the Singer Tract might be, and the birds forced to move, there is a possibility that the birds could be trapped and moved to other areas. Since the chances are rather small that the birds would become well established in a new place, it would be little more than a last resort in taking every means possible to save the species from extinction.

The trapping and transplanting would have to be done in the non-breeding season, otherwise the birds might try to return to their nesting territory. The one spot where an Ivory-bill can be expected during the non-breeding season is at its roosting hole, and any attempt at trapping would have to be done there. The only trap that I can suggest is similar to the kind once used in catching Carolina Paroquets, a net placed over the entrance after the bird has gone to roost. The difficulty would be, of course, to get a net over a hole that is about fifty feet from the ground without scaring the bird off, and the manner of doing it would have to depend on the situation of the roost hole and the nearness of other trees. Most roosting holes are dug in dead stubs which I doubt would bear the weight of a man. The easiest way would probably be to place the net by a long pole handled from a nearby tree. Details of the method, time of the attempt, etc., would all have to be adapted to the situation. I do not know whether the time soon after the bird has entered the hole, during the night, or very early in the morning would be most likely to succeed. The ideal way would be to capture a pair of birds almost simultaneously just after they had roosted and immediately start them on their journey.

The two best areas in the Mississippi Delta to which Ivory-bills could be transplanted are a medium-sized tract of virgin timber southeast of Jonesville, Louisiana, in Concordia Parish, and another forest on Big Island, Desha County, Arkansas. Neither place could support many Ivory-bills. Other possible areas are those described in the section on Ivory-bill localities.

The cost of attempting to trap and transfer Ivory-bills would include the time and expenses of a man to locate roost holes and plan the traps and operations, employment of two or three assistants for a short time during the trapping, materials, and the transportation.

Part VI.   Summary of the Ecology, Life History and Conservation of the Ivory-billed Woodpecker

FOR the three years, 1937 through 1939, an intensive study of the Ivory-billed Woodpecker was made by the writer working on a fellowship established for that purpose by the National Audubon Society; objective of the fellowship was to gather the knowledge needed to plan a conservation program for this vanishing species. About two-thirds of the time was spent in the present and former range of the bird, the southeastern United States, observing it in the field and investigating its habitat. Information contained in the literature was examined for additional records and observations.

The Ivory-billed Woodpecker once ranged throughout the swampy forests in the humid division of the Lower Austral Zone and in the Tropical Zone of Florida. Its habitat outside of Florida is the bottomland forests where sweet gum and oaks predominate; in and near Florida it is in cypress swamps and swampy hammocks. The maximum abundance of the Ivory-bill is estimated to have been one pair of birds to about six square miles of suitable habitat.

The distribution and numbers of the Ivory-bill began to decrease in the latter part of the 19th century. The periods of greatest restriction of the Ivory-bill range outside of Florida appear to have been from 1895 to 1900 and from 1915 to 1930, while in Florida the greatest decrease occurred between 1900 and 1915. Diminution of the Ivory-bill's range has coincided with the spread of the logging industry, and the birds have disappeared as the timber in the swampy forests was cut.

At least forty-nine different localities throughout the southeastern and south-central states were investigated for the possible present-day occurrence of Ivory-bills. About five areas in Louisiana, Florida, and possibly South Carolina were found to be inhabited by the woodpeckers or to have evidence of their presence; the total population of the birds I estimate (1939) to be around twenty-four individuals.

When the food supply is sufficient, the woodpecker is probably resident or sedentary, with a feeding range from three to four miles across. There is considerable evidence that pairs or individuals sometimes move long distances in search of forests supplying an adequate quantity of food.

The primary food of the Ivory-bills consists of wood-boring insect larvae, particularly larval Cerambycids, Buprestids, and Elaterids that live between the bark and the sapwood of recently dead trees. In the Mississippi Delta the woodpecker secures most of its food from the larger sweet gum, Nuttall's oak, and hackberry trees. It also feeds upon fruits, nuts, seeds, and similar vegetable material on occasion.

The Ivory-bill is present only in forests where dead and dying trees are frequent and other woodpeckers are abundant, conditions which normally prevail only in tracts of uncut, mature timber. Studies made in the Singer Tract, Louisiana, together with several recorded incidents, indicate that the ranges and numbers of individuals have been affected by the abundance of food, birds inhabiting only those areas supplying a large amount of food. The kinds of borers eaten primarily by Ivory-bills were found to be much less abundant in the forest than the kinds eaten largely or entirely by Pileated Woodpeckers, a similar but common and widespread species, and furthermore these borers are likely to be sporadically distributed and to fluctuate considerably in numbers from year to year.

Competitors or predators apparently do not seriously affect the Ivory-bill in any way. It was killed by man for various reasons, but chiefly because collectors desired specimens. Shooting has become an increasingly dangerous threat to the existence of the species as the number of individuals has diminished.

The daily activities of the woodpeckers during the non-breeding season follow a fairly definite pattern. Beginning about sunrise, they feed and move actively during the early morning; they are quiet during the middle of the day, feed again in

99

late afternoon, and then end the day by going to roost about dusk. Ivory-bills roost singly in holes, and very frequently use the same hole night after night; one pair of birds has used the same roosting ground for three years. They apparently do not use old nesting cavities for roosting holes, but dig others for this purpose.

Ivory-bills usually travel in pairs, and after the nesting season until the following fall or winter, often in family groups; beyond this they apparently have no tendency to flock or associate with others. The Ivory-bill is not unusually wary of man nor seriously affected by man's presence.

No observations were made indicating that the birds have nesting territories which they defend from other Ivory-bills. The courtship is a brief ceremony consisting of the pair touching or clasping bills, sometimes accompanied by low calls.

The Ivory-bill breeds at varying times from January to May; no cause for this wide variation in nesting times was found. The nest cavity is dug in a dead or partially dead tree. The number of eggs in a nest usually varies from one to four, with the average being 2.9 per nest. Nests begun in January or February contained one or two eggs or young a piece, while those begun in April or May usually contained from three to four eggs or young.

Incubation of the eggs lasts about twenty days. Both sexes incubate, the male staying on the nest overnight. Nestlings remain in the nest about five weeks, where they are fed by both parents, and brooded by the male at night and occasionally during the day. After leaving the nest, young birds are fed by the adults for two months or longer. Even after becoming independent, they frequently remain with the parents until late fall or winter.

Of six Ivory-bill nests in northern Louisiana, three were known to have been successful and three were mysteriously destroyed. In nine broods of young out of the nest, an average of 2.11 young per brood was observed. The percentage of nesting success of the Ivory-bill is approximate

to that of the Pileated Woodpecker and the Song Sparrow, but the Ivory-bill usually lays fewer eggs. No definite factor was found appearing to lower the reproductive success of the species.

The only factors discovered which have definitely affected the numbers and distribution of the species are the quantity of food available to the birds and their destruction by man. The numbers of wood-boring insects have been vastly decreased by logging of the southern swamps, which has destroyed the large, mature forests where the Ivory-bill could find sufficient food. This has been a more general and widespread factor than has shooting.

Mature forests of large, old trees have almost disappeared, and these conditions favorable for the Ivory-billed Woodpecker will very probably never again prevail. Its preservation must be accomplished by saving suitable habitat or by maintaining on certain areas an adequate food supply for the birds.

Ideal measures for the conservation of the Ivory-billed Woodpecker would be to preserve in their entirety areas inhabited by the bird, as refuges and as primitive areas. The most important areas in the country are the Singer Tract in Louisiana, the Big Cypress and lower Apalachicola River swamps in Florida, and possibly parts of the Santee River swamp in South Carolina.

The area necessary for an Ivory-billed Woodpecker refuge would be about two and a half to three square miles of good habitat for each pair of the birds. Where the chief obstacle to the establishment of a refuge is the high value of the timber, as in the Singer Tract, a program of selective cutting is recommended whereby sound and valuable timber may be cut and sold, leaving dead and dying trees to supply borers to the woodpeckers. The quantity of woodpecker food may be artificially increased by killing certain trees.

The Ivory-bill must be granted complete protection from man by the barring of all hunters and collectors from areas inhabited by the woodpecker.

APPENDIX

A. Nomenclature

THE Ivory-billed Woodpecker was first described by Mark Catesby and named the 'Largest White-bill Woodpecker,' *Picus maximus rostro albo* (Catesby, 1731; 1:16). Linnaeus named the bird *Picus principalis* (Linné, 1758; Tom 1:113). G. R. Gray erected the genus *Campephilus* (Gray, 1940; 54), with the Ivory-bill as type species, giving it its present name, *Campephilus principalis* (Linnaeus). (*Campephilus*: Gr.—*kampe*, caterpillar; *philus*, loving.)

The synonymy of the species includes:

Dryocopus principalis (Boie, 1828; Isis, **21**:326)
Dendrocopus principalis (Bonaparte, 1838; 39)
(*Campephilus*) *principalis* (Cabanis and Heine, 1863; **2**:100)
Megapicos principalis (Malherbe, 1849; **30**:318)

Common names for the species, besides the recognized 'Ivory-billed Woodpecker,' are mostly based on the white bill or large size of the bird, and many are modifications of names applied to the ordinary Pileated Woodpecker. Some names are derived from the bird's call. W. L. McAtee has collected the following common names for the bird:

Ivory-bill
Pearly bill or Pearl-bill
Log-god
Log-cock, Big, or Large, or White-billed
White-billed Woodpecker, or Woodcock, or Logcock
Big or King Woodchuck
White-back Woodpecker (in northern Florida)
King of the Woodpeckers
Indian Hen
Southern Giant Woodpecker
Pate or Pait (in western Florida)
Ivory-billed Caip
Tit-ka (Seminole name)
Grand Pic Noir a bec blanc
Poule de bois (in southern Louisiana)
Grand pique-bois (in southern Louisiana)

Other common names not included in the above list:

Le Pic noir hupe de la Caroline (Brisson, 1760)
Pic a bec d'ivoire (Valenciennes, 1826)
Haubenspecht (Borowski, 1781)
Elfenbeinschnabel-Specht (Koch, 1888)
Kent (in northern Louisiana)

B. Taxonomy and Related Species

The Ivory-billed Woodpecker is included in the family Picidae, subfamily Picinae, genus *Campephilus*. The characters separating the genus *Campephilus* from others of the Picidae are described by Ridgway (1914), who also presents a key to the three species of the genus, *imperialis*, *principalis*, and *bairdii*.

The Imperial Woodpecker (*Campephilus imperialis* (Gould)) is the largest woodpecker in the world, averaging 565 mm. or about 22 inches in length. Ridgway (1914) gives as the range of the species "northwestern Mexico, in States of Sonora, Chihuahua, Durango, Zacatecas, Jalisco, and Michoacan."

Nelson (1898) and Salvin and Godman (1895) have given the most complete accounts of the species. It inhabits the pine forests of the Sierras of northwestern Mexico, a chain of table-like mountains forested largely with *Pinus montezuma*. Nelson found the birds preferring park-like country, and feeding on dead pines.

Kelly Simmons, living in Chihuahua, wrote me (April 1941) that Imperial Woodpeckers were easily found, although not common, in the high pine timber at an altitude of from 7500 to 9000 feet along the Sonora-Chihuahua line.

Many of the habits of the Imperial seem to be similar to those of the Ivory-billed Woodpecker. Nelson describes the calls of the larger bird as being "queer, nasal, penny-trumpet-like notes." Simmons wrote that they always seemed to be found in pairs, which "return each evening to a certain tree or group of dead trees," probably for roosting. They apparently nest in February, Nelson reporting a set of two eggs taken at that date. Salvin and Godman state that a juvenal male, collected on May 18, had large white tips to the primaries, thus resembling the juvenal Ivory-bill.

A. P. Smith (1908) reports that one man in west central Chihuahua shot seventeen Imperial Woodpeckers in a few months, cutting off the bills which he thought to be the valuable part of the bird.

The Cuban Ivory-billed Woodpecker (*Campephilus bairdii* Cassin) was also known by the native name of "carpentero real" (Gundlach, 1866). Barbour (1923) gives its former range as in the Organ Mountains north of San Diego de Los Banos; in the lowland, mixed hardwood forests about the Ensenando de Cochinos; near Guantanamo, Banaquises, Calimete, and along the Hanabana. It has disappeared as the result of the felling of the lowland forests which began in early colonial times and increased when the sugar industry grew so rapidly. Bond (1936) states that the bird is now present in the little-known Sierra De Cristal in Oriente, possibly in the Zapata swamp.

Barbour stated that its voice was like a boy's tin trumpet, that the bird usually flew in families, and that its eggs were never found.

The Guatemalan Ivory-billed Woodpeckers and other white-billed woodpeckers of the tropics belong to the genus *Scapaneus* which, compared with *Campephilus*, has a smaller less-depressed bill, a larger outer primary, less feather development in the chin and orbital region, and barred instead of uniform black underparts.

C. PLUMAGES AND ANATOMY

The nestling Ivory-bill has never been seen just after hatching. It is probably naked, although Scott (1888) states that a young bird about "one-third grown" had feathers just beginning to cover the down. None of the nests I have examined contained any remains of down feathers.

The juvenal plumage is similar to an adult female's (Plate 20, and section on the care and growth of young after leaving the nest), but in a young female specimen (M.C.Z. No. 242972) collected on April 15, 1892, near Old Town, Florida, the black of the plumage is almost entirely non-iridescent, the white lines on neck and back are less well defined, seeming broader, and all primaries are tipped with white, increasing from a slight tip on outer primary to one inch on the fourth (from inside) and two inches on the secondaries.

Chapin (1921) describes the juvenal Ivory-bill as having the two inner primaries abbreviated, in common with other woodpeckers. In the specimen mentioned above he described the inner primary as measuring 19 mm. long and being covered by a sheath, the second as measuring 91 mm. and being without a sheath, and the third equaling 131 mm. and having no sheath. He considered the first primary as probably not being a true juvenal feather.

The young male birds whose development I have watched in the field first showed red feathers in the crest when they were about two and a half months out of the nest, and by the middle of August the plumage pattern was almost identical with that of an adult. The post-juvenal molt is probably complete by the end of summer.

The following description of the adult plumage is modified from Ridgway (1914):

Adult Male: General color glossy blue-black, the primaries and tail duller black, or with bluish gloss less distinct; nasal plumes, stripes on side of head and neck (commencing usually beneath middle of eye and much narrower on the anterior portion) white, these stripes continued posteriorly along each edge of interscapular region; secondaries (except basal portion), terminal portion of primaries, except five or six outermost, and under wing-coverts white; occipital portion of crest scarlet, front and top black.

Adult Female: Similar in coloration to the adult male, crest wholly glossy blue-black and more recurved than that of the male.

In 87 Ivory-bill specimens examined, the outermost primary tipped with white was the 4th (counting from the inside) in 64% of the cases, the 5th in 25%, the 6th in 7%, and the 3rd in 3%. About one-fifth of the specimens had white spots near the ends of the outer pair of tail feathers, and several had the broad flank feathers tipped with white.

The only other plumage variations observed were those of a male from Punta Rassa, Florida, which had the inner vane of the fourth primary of one wing almost entirely white, and a female from Florida that had parts of the plumage, especially ends of the primaries, brownish.

Ivory-bill specimens collected in July, August,

and September all showed signs of molt, but there is not enough material to be able to understand the sequence. The specimen in heaviest molt, collected on August 23 in Florida, had several tail feathers missing, and the seventh primary was growing in as were many crown feathers.

The bill of a juvenal bird just out of the nest is chalky white; with a temporary dark marking near the end of the culmen; it gradually deepens in color until by the time the bird has been out of the nest for three months it is an ivory-white color. The bills of old skins have darkened to a brownish yellow. Ridgway describes the legs and feet of adults to be "(in life) light gray, the larger scutella paler and somewhat yellowish gray, the claws horn gray or pale horn color." The juvenal birds did not differ in this respect.

Hargitt (1890), quoting the notes of W. E. D. Scott on a juvenal female Ivory-bill, writes: "Eyes not open. Irides, on dissection, greyish yellow." The juvenal birds I observed had eyes dark brown or sepia in color, with the eyelid a dark red. The eye lightens gradually until, at about the end of the third or fourth month out of the nest, it is the clear lemon-yellow of the adults. The eyelid of an adult is orange.

The most complete published description of the internal anatomy of the Ivory-bill is by Audubon, in his 'Ornithological Biography' (1839, **5**: 525–533), also in 'Birds of America' (1856, **4**: 219–226). His description indicates that the anatomy differs little from that of the Pileated Woodpecker. Maynard describes and figures (1896, Pl. XIX) the sternum of the Ivory-bill and also describes the syrinx.

D. MEASUREMENTS

Ridgway (1914) gives as the average measurements of fifteen adult male specimens (in mm.): for length, 454; wing, 255.8; tail, 154.4; culmen, 68.2; tarsus, 44.2; outer anterior toe, 32.1. The average measurements of eleven adult females are: for length, 471; wing, 256.4; tail, 159.5; culmen, 64.3; tarsus, 42.6; outer anterior toe, 31.7.

The following table shows the means and standard deviations for bill and wing measurements made on Ivory-bill specimens from different regions of the bird's range.

South Carolina and Georgia

	Number specimens	Bill Mean	Bill Standard deviation	Wing Mean	Wing Standard deviation
Male	1	71.9	x	257	x
Female	2	67.8	x	258	x

Florida

	Number specimens	Bill Mean	Bill Standard deviation	Wing Mean	Wing Standard deviation
Male	38	74.0	2.8	256	4.4
Female	38	70.1	2.8	254	5.8

Mississippi Delta and Adjoining Regions

	Number specimens	Bill Mean	Bill Standard deviation	Wing Mean	Wing Standard deviation
Male	8	74.1	2.6	257	4.2
Female	4	70.2	2.2	262	7.1

Laurent (1917) gives $31\frac{1}{2}$ inches (800 mm.) as the measured extent of a Florida male, and 30 inches (788 mm.) of a Florida female.

Catesby (1731) states that the weight of an Ivory-bill is 20 ounces. The label of a male specimen (M.C.Z. No. 35888) collected on January 17, 1877, in Hernando County, Florida, records the weight as one pound.

E. SCIENTIFIC NAMES OF BIRDS, MAMMALS AND REPTILES MENTIONED IN TEXT

BIRDS (arranged according to the A. O. U. 'Check-List,' 4th edition)

Heron	Ardeinae
Bittern	Botaurinae
Ibis	Threskiornithinae
Pintail	*Dafila acuta tzitzihoa*
Vulture	Cathartidae
Cooper's Hawk	*Accipiter cooperi*
Red-tailed Hawk	*Buteo borealis*
Red-shouldered Hawk	*Buteo lineatus*
Duck Hawk	*Falco peregrinus anatum*
Sparrow Hawk	*Falco s. sparverius*
Ruffed Grouse	*Bonasa umbellus*
Turkey	*Meleagris gallopavo*
Carolina Paroquet	*Conuropsis c. carolinensis*
Barred Owl	*Strix varia*
Flicker	*Colaptes auratus*
Pileated Woodpecker	*Ceophloeus pileatus*
Florida Pileated Woodpecker	*Ceophloeus p. floridanus*
Southern Pileated Woodpecker	*Ceophloeus p. pileatus*
Red-bellied Woodpecker	*Centurus carolinus*
Red-headed Woodpecker	*Melanerpes erythrocephalus*
Hairy Woodpecker	*Dryobates villosus*
Downy Woodpecker	*Dryobates pubescens*
Ivory-billed Woodpecker	*Campephilus principalis*
Cuban Ivory-billed Woodpecker	*Campephilus bairdii*

Imperial Woodpecker	*Campephilus imperialis*
Guatemalan Ivory-billed Woodpecker	*Phloeoceastes guatemalensis*
Phoebe	*Sayornis phoebe*
Tufted Titmouse	*Baeolophus bicolor*
Red-breasted Nuthatch	*Sitta canadensis*
White-breasted Nuthatch	*Sitta carolinensis*
House Wren	*Troglodytes a. aedon*
Carolina Wren	*Thryothorus ludovicianus*
Louisiana Water-Thrush	*Seiurus motacilla*
Redstart	*Setophaga ruticilla*
Cardinal	*Richmondena cardinalis*
Towhee	*Pipilo erythrophthalmus*
Song Sparrow	*Melospiza melodia*

MAMMALS

Opossum	*Didelphis*
Bear	*Euarctos*
Raccoon	*Procyon*
Wolf	*Canis*
Deer	*Odocoileus*
Panther	*Felis*
Bob-cat	*Lynx*

REPTILES

Alligator	*Alligator mississippiensis*

F. SCIENTIFIC NAMES OF TREE SPECIES MENTIONED IN TEXT (Principally Following SARGENT's 'Manual of the Trees of North America,' 2nd Edition)

Apple, pond	*Annona glabra* L.
Ash, green	*Fraxinus pennsylvanica* var. *lanceolata* Sarg.
Ash, water	*Fraxinus caroliniana* Mill.
Bay, swamp	*Persea palustris* Sarg.
Bay, sweet	*Magnolia virginiana* L.

Beech, blue (ironwood)	*Carpinus caroliniana* Walt.
Cedar, red	*Juniperus virginiana* L.
Cottonwood	*Populus deltoides* Sudw. or *Populus heterophylla* L.
Cypress, bald	*Taxodium distichum* Rich.
Cypress, pond	*Taxodium ascendens* Brong.
Elm, American	*Ulmus americana* L.
Elm, cedar	*Ulmus crassifolia* Nutt.
Fig, wild	*Ficus aurea* Nutt.
Gum, black (sour)	*Nyssa sylvatica* Marsh.
Gum, sweet	*Liquidambar styraciflua* L.
Gum, tupelo	*Nyssa aquatica* Marsh.
Hackberry	*Celtis laevigata* Willd.
Hickory, water	*Carya aquatica* Nutt.
Holly	*Ilex opaca* Ait.
Locust, honey	*Gleditsia triacanthos* L.
Locust, water	*Gleditsia aquatica* Marsh.
Magnolia	*Magnolia grandiflora* L.
Maple, red	*Acer rubrum* L.
Oak, cherrybark (red)	*Quercus rubra* var. *pagodaefolia* Ashe.
Oak, cow	*Quercus prinus* L.
Oak, laurel	*Quercus laurifolia* Michx.
Oak, live	*Quercus virginiana* Mill.
Oak, Nuttall's	*Quercus nuttallii* Palmer.
Oak, overcup	*Quercus lyrata* Walt.
Oak, post (delta)	*Quercus mississippiensis* Ashe.
Oak, water	*Quercus nigra* L.
Oak, white	*Quercus alba* L.
Oak, willow	*Quercus phellos* L.
Palm, royal	*Roystonea regia* Cook.
Palmetto, cabbage	*Sabal palmetto* R. & S.
Pecan	*Carya pecan* Engl. & Garebn.
Persimmon	*Diospyros virginiana* L.
Pine, loblolly	*Pinus taeda* L.
Pine, long-leaf	*Pinus palustris* Mill.
Pine, slash	*Pinus caribaea* Morel.

REFERENCES CITED

ANON.
1879. (Linnean Soc. report). Forest & Stream, **12**: 126.
1885. Forest & Stream, **24**: 508.
ALLEN, ARTHUR A.
1939. Ivory-billed Woodpecker. *In* Life histories of North American woodpeckers, by A. C. Bent. Bull. U. S. Nat. Mus., no. 174: 1–12.
ALLEN, A. A., AND KELLOGG, P. P.
1937. Recent observations on the Ivory-billed Woodpecker. Auk, **54**: 164–184.
ALLEN, J. A.
1871. On the mammals and winter birds of east Florida. Bull. Mus. Comp. Zool., Harv., **2**: 301, 393.
1893. List of mammals and birds collected in northeastern Sonora and northwestern Chihuahua, Mexico. Bull. Amer. Mus. Nat. Hist., **5**: 35.
AMERICAN ORNITHOLOGISTS' UNION
1931. Check-list of North American birds. 4th ed. Lancaster, Pa. P. 201.
ARTHUR, STANLEY C.
1918. The birds of Louisiana. Bull. La. Dept. Cons., no. 5: 53.
AUDUBON, JOHN JAMES
1831–39. Ornithological biography. Edinburgh. Vol. 1: 341–347; 5: 525, 533.
1842. Birds of America. New York. Vol. 4: 214–226.
AVERY, W. C.
1890. Birds observed in Alabama. Amer. Field, **34**: 608.
BAILEY, A. M.
1939. Ivory-billed Woodpecker's beak in an Indian grave in Colorado. Condor, **41**: 164.
BAILEY, H. B.
1883. Memoranda of a collection of eggs from Georgia. Bull. Nuttall Ornith. Club, **8**: 40.
BAILEY, H. H.
1925. The birds of Florida   Baltimore. P. 81, pl. 44.
1927. The Ivory-billed Woodpecker in Florida. Auk, **44**: 18–20.
BAIRD, S. F., BREWER, T. M., AND RIDGWAY, R.
1875. A history of North American birds. Boston. Vol. 2: 491–493, 496–499.
BARBOUR, THOMAS
1923. The birds of Cuba. Memoirs Nuttall Ornith. Club, no. 6: 91.
BAYNARD, O. E.
1909. Echoes from Florida. Oologist, **26**: 5–7.
1913. Breeding birds of Alachua county, Florida. Auk, **30**: 245.
1914. Two months in the Everglades. Oologist, **31**: 36.
1937. A check-list of the birds of Highlands Hammock State Park. (mimeog.).
BEAL, F. E. L.
1911. Food of the woodpeckers of the United States. Bull. U. S. Bur. Biol. Surv., no. 37: 62–63.
BENDIRE, CHARLES
1895. Life histories of North American birds, from the parrots to the grackles. Spec. Bull. U. S. Nat. Mus., **3**: 42–45.
BEYER, G. E.
1900. The Ivory-billed Woodpecker in Louisiana. Auk, **17**: 97–99.
BLACKMAN, M. W., AND STAGE, H. H.
1924. On the succession of insects living in the bark and wood of dying, dead, and decaying hickory. Tech. Pub. N. Y. S. Col. Forestry, **17**: 3–269.
BOARDMAN, G. A.
1885. The big woodpeckers. Forest & Stream, **24**: 388.
BOIE, F.
1828. Ornithologishe Beutrage. Isis, **21**: 326.
BONAPARTE, C. L.
1838. Geographical and comparative list of the birds of Europe and North America. London. P. 39.

BOND, JAMES
1936. Birds of the West Indies. Philadelphia.
BREWSTER, WILLIAM
1881. With the birds on a Florida river. Bull. Nuttall Ornith. Club, **6**: 41–42.
BREWSTER, W., AND CHAPMAN, F. M.
1891. Notes on the birds of the lower Suwanee River. Auk, **8**: 136, 137.
BRYANT, HENRY
1859. Birds observed in eastern Florida south of St. Augustine. Proc. Boston Soc. Nat. Hist., **7**: 11.
BURNETT, WALDO I.
1854. Proc. Boston Soc. Nat. Hist., **4**: 116.
BUTLER, A. W.
1931. Some bird records from Florida. Auk, **48**: 438.
CABANIS, J., AND HEINE, F.
1863. Museum Heineanum, 4: heft. 2: 100.
CAMPBELL, J. S., KUHN, J. J., LOWERY, G. H., SR., AND LOWERY, G. H., JR.
1934. Bird-Lore's thirty-fourth Christmas census. (Tallulah, La.) Bird-Lore, **36**: 55.
CATESBY, MARK
1731. Natural history of Carolina, Florida and the Bahama Islands. London, Vol. 1: 16.
CHAPIN, J. P.
1921. The abbreviated inner primaries of nestling woodpeckers. Auk, **38**: 533, 539, 540.
CHAPMAN, F. M.
1930. Notes on the plumage of North American birds: Ivory-billed Woodpecker. Bird-Lore, **32**: 265–267.
1932. Handbook of birds of eastern North America. 2nd rev. ed., 1932. New York. P. 362.
CHRISTY, B. H.
1939. Northern Pileated Woodpecker. *In* Life histories of North American Woodpeckers, by A. C. Bent. Bull. U. S. Nat. Mus., no. 174: 181.
CLARKE, S. C.
1885. The Ivory-billed Woodpecker in Florida. Forest & Stream, **24**: 367.
COAHOMA
1888. The Pileated Woodpecker. Forest & Stream, **31**: 122.
COOKE, W. W.
1888. Report on bird migration in the Mississippi valley in the years 1884 and 1885. U. S. Dept. Agric., Bull. Div. Econ. Ornith., **2**: 127–128.
1914. Some winter birds of Oklahoma. Auk, **31**: 480.
CORRINGTON, J. D.
1922. The winter birds of the Biloxi, Mississippi, region. Auk, **39**: 545.
CORY, C. B.
1919. Catalogue of the birds of the Americas. Pub. Field Mus. Nat. Hist. (Zool. Series, 13), pt. 2: 461–462.
COTTAM, CLARENCE, AND KNAPPEN, PHOEBE
1939. Food of some uncommon North American birds. Auk, **56**: 162.
COUES, ELLIOTT, AND YARROW, H. C.
1878. Notes on the natural history of Ft. Macon, N.C., and vicinity. Proc. Phila. Acad. Nat. Sci., **1878**: 22.
CRABB, E. D.
1925. A list of woodpeckers found in Oklahoma prior to 1924. Proc. Okla. Acad. Sci., **4**: 28.
1930. The woodpeckers of Oklahoma. Pub. Univ. Okla., **2**: 113, 117–118.
D., W. A.
1885. The great woodpeckers. Forest & Stream, **24**: 427.
DAVIE, OLIVER
1898. Nests and eggs of North American birds. Columbus. P. 209.

DRESSER, H. E.
  1865. Notes on the birds of southern Texas. Ibis, n.s. 1: 468.
DUTCHER, WILLIAM
  1905. Report of A. O. U. committee for protection of North American birds. Auk, 22: 111.
ELLIS, J. B.
  1917. Forty years ago and more. Oologist, 34: 2–4.
  1918. Ivory-billed Woodpecker not yet extinct. Oologist, 35: 11–12.
FEATHERSTONAUGH, G. W.
  1835. Geological report of an examination made in 1834 of the elevated country between the Missouri and Red Rivers. Washington. P. 72.
GORDON, THEODORE
  1909. Ivory-billed Woodpecker. Forest & Stream, 72: 972.
GOSSE, P. H.
  1859. Letters from Alabama. London. Pp. 91–93.
GRAHAM, S. C.
  1909. The Ivory-billed Woodpecker. Forest & Stream, 72: 892.
GRAY, G. R.
  1840. A list of the genera of birds. London. P. 54.
GUNDLACH, JOHANN
  1866. Revista y catalogo de les aves Cubanas.
GUNDLACH, JEAN
  1874. Neue beitrage zur ornithologie Cubas. Journ. f. Ornith., 22: 148–150.
H., J. M.
  1885. Forest & Stream, 24: 388.
HARGITT, E.
  1890. Catalogue of birds of the British museum. London. 18: 463–465.
HASBROUCK, E. M.
  1891. The present status of the Ivory-billed Woodpecker (Campephilus principalis). Auk, 8: 174–186.
HAYMOND, RUFUS
  1869. Birds of Franklin county, Indiana. First Ann. Report Ind. Geol. Surv., p. 211.
HENNINGER, W. F.
  1917. The diary of a New England ornithologist. Wilson Bull., 29: 4.
HOWE, R. H., AND KING, LEROY
  1902. Notes on various Florida birds. Contr. N. A. Ornith., 1: 30.
HOWELL, A. H.
  1907. Birds of Alabama. U. S. Bur. Biol. Surv. Pp. 159–162.
  1911. Birds of Arkansas. Bull. U. S. Bur. Biol. Surv., no. 38: 45–46.
  1932. Florida bird life. New York. Pp. 313–315.
HOXIE, WALTER
  1885. Notes on birds of the Sea Islands. Ornith. & Oologist, 10: 62.
  1887. Probable occurrence of the Ivory-billed Woodpecker on Pritchard's Island, S.C. Ornith. & Oologist, 12: 122.
HOYT, R. D.
  1905. Nesting of the Ivory-billed Woodpecker in Florida. Warbler (2nd ser.), 1: 52–55.
JAMES, EDWIN
  1905. Account of an expedition from Pittsburgh to the Rocky Mountains. R. G. Thwaites, ed. Early Western Travels. Cleveland. 16: 72.
KENNARD, F. H.
  1915. On the trail of the Ivory-bill. Auk, 32: 1–14.
KLINE, H. A.
  1886. Ivory-billed Woodpecker. Forest & Stream, 26: 163.
  1887. Florida bird notes. Forest & Stream, 28: 412–413.
KOCH, AUGUST
  1888. Zwei Monate in west Florida. Mittheilungen des Ornithologischen Vereines in Wien, 12: 1, 2, 26.
KUBICHEK, W. F.
  1936. The Survey, 17: 34.
LAURENT, PHILIP
  1887. Notes on birds of Levy county, Florida. Ornith. & Oolo-

gist, 12: 157–159.
  1917. My Ivory-billed Woodpeckers. Oologist, 34: 65–67.
LEOPOLD, ALDO
  1933. Game management. New York.
LINNÉ, C.
  1758. Systema naturae 10th ed., vol. 1: 113.
LINSDALE, J. M.
  1933. The nesting season of birds in Doniphan county, Kansas. Condor, 35: 155–160.
LOWERY, G. H.
  1935. The Ivory-billed Woodpecker in Louisiana. Proc. La. Acad. Sci., 2: 84–86.
MALHERBE, ALFRED
  1849. Nouvelle classification des picinées on pics. Memoirs Academia, Metz, 30: 318.
MARBUT, C. F.
  1935. Soils of the United States. U. S. Bur. Soils.
MAYNARD, C. J.
  1896. The birds of eastern North America. Pp. 371–373.
McILHENNY, E. A.
  1941. The passing of the Ivory-billed Woodpecker. Auk, 58: 582–584.
MERRIAM, C. H.
  1874. Ornithological notes from the south. Amer. Naturalist 8: 88.
MOSELEY, E. L.
  1928. The abundance of woodpeckers and other birds in northeastern Louisiana. Wilson Bull., 40: 115–116.
MURPHEY, E. E.
  1937. Observations of the bird life of the middle Savannah valley, 1890–1937. Contr. Charleston Mus., 9: 29.
MURPHY, R. C.
  1929. A second topotype of Campephilus principalis. Auk, 46: 376.
NEHRLING, H.
  1882. List of birds observed at Houston, Harris Co., Texas, and in the counties Montgomery, Galveston, and Fort Bend. Bull. Nuttall Ornith. Club, 7: 170.
NELSON, E. W.
  1898. The Imperial Ivory-billed Woodpecker, Campephilus imperialis (Gould). Auk, 15: 217–223.
NICE, MARGARET M.
  1931. The birds of Oklahoma. Rev. ed. Pub. Univ. Okla., 3: 116.
  1937. Studies in the life history of the Song Sparrow, I. Trans. Linn. Soc. N.Y., IV.
NICHOLSON, D. J.
  1926. My first Ivory-billed Woodpecker. Oologist, 43: 156–158.
OBERHOLSER, H. C.
  1938. The bird life of Louisiana. Bull. La. Dept. Cons., no. 28: 380–382.
PEARSON, T. G.
  1932. Protection of the Ivory-billed Woodpecker. Bird-Lore, 34: 300–301.
  1937. Handsome Flickers and a rare cousin. In The book of birds, ed. by Gilbert Grosvenor and Alexander Wetmore. Nat. Geog. Soc., Washington. Vol. 2: 65, 73.
PENNANT, THOMAS
  1742. Arctic zoology, 1: 314–315.
PENNOCK, C. J.
  1901. Recent capture of Ivory-billed Woodpeckers in Florida. Proc. Del. Valley Ornith. Club, 4: 8.
PENNOCK, C. J. (JOHN WILLIAMS)
  1917. Some notes from St. Marks, Florida. Wilson Bull., 29: 165–166.
  1920. Notes on the birds of Wakulla county, Florida. Wilson Bull., 32: 10.
PHELPS, F. M.
  1914. The resident bird life of the Big Cypress swamp region. Wilson Bull., 26: 99.
PHILLIP, P. B.
  1915. Abstr. Proc. Linn. Soc. N.Y. for 1914, p. 2.

PHILLIPS, J. C.
1926. An attempt to list the extinct and vanishing birds of the western hemisphere. Verhandlungen VI Internationalen Ornithologen-Kongresses Kopenhagen, pp. 512–513.
PINDAR, L. O.
1889. List of the birds of Fulton county, Kentucky. Auk, 6: 313.
1924. Winter birds in eastern Arkansas. Wilson Bull., 36: 205.
1925. Birds of Fulton county, Kentucky. Wilson Bull., 37: 86.
PUTNAM, J. A., AND BULL, HENRY
1932. The trees of the bottomlands of the Mississippi River delta region. South. Forest Exp. Stat., Occ. Paper, 27.
RIDGWAY, ROBERT
1874. Catalogue of the birds ascertained to occur in Illinois. Ann. Lyceum Nat. Hist., N.Y., 10: 377.
1881. A catalogue of the birds of Illinois. Ill. State Lab. Nat. Hist., I; Bull. 4: 185.
1889. The ornithology of Illinois. Ill. Nat. Hist. Surv., Springfield. Vol. 1: 374–376.
1898. The home of the Ivory-bill. Osprey, 3: 35–36.
1914. The birds of North and Middle America. Bull. U. S. Nat. Mus., no. 50. Vol. 6: 167–169.
1915. Bird-life in southern Illinois. Bird-Lore, 17: 194.
ROEMER, FERDINAND
1849. Texas. P. 461.
SALVIN, OSBERT, AND GODMAN, F. D.
1895. Aves Biologia Centrali Americana. Vol. 2. London.
SARGENT, C. S.
1884. Report on the forests of North America. U. S. D. I. census office.
SCHMAUS, MARTIN
1938. Beitr. Fortpflanzungsbiol. der Vogel, 14(5): 181–184.
SCOTT, W. E. D.
1881. On birds observed in Sumpter, Levy, and Hillsboro, counties, Florida. Bull. Nuttall Ornith. Club, 6: 16.
1888. Supplementary notes from the Gulf coast of Florida, with a description of a new species of Marsh Wren. Auk, 5: 185, 186.
1889. A summary of observations on the birds of the Gulf coast of Florida. Auk, 6: 251.
1892. Notes on the birds of the Caloosahatchie region of Florida. Auk, 9: 212, 218.
1898. Bird studies. New York. Pp. 309, 310, 335.
1904. The story of a bird lover. New York. Pp. 158, 160–161, 267–270.
SHELLEY, L. O.
1932. Inbreeding Downy Woodpeckers. Bird-Banding, 3: 69–70.
1935. A pair of Downy Woodpeckers mated during four consecutive years. Bird-Banding, 6: 135–136.

SHUFELDT, R. W.
1890. A skeleton of the Ivory-bill. Forest & Stream, 35: 431.
SMITH, A. P.
1908. Destruction of Imperial Woodpeckers. Condor, 10: 91.
SNEDECOR, G. W.
1938. Statistical methods. Ames, Iowa. Pp. 67–77.
TANNER, J. T.
1938. Bird-Lore's thirty-eighth Christmas census. (Singer Tract.) Bird-Lore, 40: 54.
TAYLOR, G. C.
1862. Five weeks in the peninsula of Florida, 1861. Ibis, 4: 128, 133, 135.
THOMPSON, MAURICE
1885. A red-headed family. By-ways and bird-notes. New York. Pp. 23–39.
1889. A red-headed family. Oologist, 6: 23–29.
1896. An archer's sojourn in the Okefinokee. Atlantic Monthly, April. Pp. 486–491.
VOGT, WILLIAM, CAHALANE, VICTOR, COTTAM, CLARENCE, AND LEOPOLD, ALDO
1939. Report of the committee on bird protection, 1938. Auk, 56: 212–213.
WAYNE, A. T.
1893. Additional notes on the birds of the Suwanee River. Auk, 10: 338.
1895. Notes on the birds of the Wacissa and Aucilla River regions of Florida. Auk, 12: 364, 366–367.
1905. A rare plumage of the Ivory-billed Woodpecker. Auk, 22: 414.
1910. Birds of South Carolina. Contr. Charleston Mus. Pp. 87–88.
WHITEHEAD, R. B.
1907. A preliminary catalog of the birds of Missouri. Trans. Acad. Sci. St. Louis, 17: 119.
WILLIAMS, R. W., JR.
1904. A preliminary list of the birds of Leon county, Florida. Auk, 21: 455.
WILSON, ALEXANDER
1811. American ornithology. Philadelphia. Vol. 4: 20–26, pl. 29.
WILSON, KENNETH A.
1938. Owl studies at Ann Arbor, Michigan. Auk, 55: 193.
WINTERS, R. K., PUTNAM, J. A., AND ELDREDGE, I. F.
1938. Forest resources of the north Louisiana delta. U. S. Dept. Agric. Misc. Pub., no. 309.
WOODHOUSE, S. W.
1853. Birds. In Rept. Exped. down Zuni and Colorado Rivers, by Capt. L. Sitgreaves. P. 90.
YELL
1885. The big woodpecker. Forest & Stream, 24. 407.

INDEX

(All italicized cross-references below refer to entries
under the heading of Woodpecker, Ivory-billed.)

109

CATALOGUE OF DOVER BOOKS

Nature

AN INTRODUCTION TO BIRD LIFE FOR BIRD WATCHERS, Aretas A. Saunders. Fine, readable introduction to birdwatching. Includes a great deal of basic information on about 160 different varieties of wild birds—elementary facts not easily found elsewhere. Complete guide to identification procedures, methods of observation, important habits of birds, finding nests, food, etc. "Could make bird watchers of readers who never suspected they were vulnerable to that particular virus," CHICAGO SUNDAY TRIBUNE. Unabridged, corrected edition. Bibliography. Index. 22 line drawings by D. D'Ostilio. Formerly "The Lives of Wild Birds." 256pp. 5⅜ x 8½. T1139 Paperbound **$1.00**

LIFE HISTORIES OF NORTH AMERICAN BIRDS, Arthur Cleveland Bent. Bent's historic, all-encompassing series on North American birds, originally produced under the auspices of the Smithsonian Institution, now being republished in its entirety by Dover Publications. The twenty-volume collection forms the most comprehensive, most complete, most-used source of information in existence. Each study describes in detail the characteristics, range, distribution, habits, migratory patterns, courtship procedures, plumage, eggs, voice, enemies, etc. of the different species and subspecies of the birds that inhabit our continent, utilizing reports of hundreds of contemporary observers as well as the writings of the great naturalists of the past. Invaluable to the ornithologist, conservationist, amateur naturalist, and birdwatcher. All books in the series contain numerous photographs to provide handy guides for identification and study.

LIFE HISTORIES OF NORTH AMERICAN BIRDS OF PREY. Including hawks, eagles, falcons, buzzards, condors, owls, etc. Index. Bibliographies of 923 items. 197 full-page plates containing close to 400 photographs. Total of 907pp. 5⅜ x 8½.
Vol. I: T931 Paperbound **$2.50**
Vol. II: T932 Paperbound **$2.50**
The set Paperbound **$5.00**

LIFE HISTORIES OF NORTH AMERICAN SHORE BIRDS. Including 81 varieties of such birds as sandpipers, woodcocks, snipes, phalaropes, oyster catchers, and many others. Index for each volume. Bibliographies of 449 entries. 121 full-page plates including over 200 photographs. Total of 860 pp. 5⅜ x 8½.
Vol. I: T933 Paperbound **$2.35**
Vol. II: T934 Paperbound **$2.35**
The set Paperbound **$4.70**

LIFE HISTORIES OF NORTH AMERICAN WILD FOWL. Including 73 varieties of ducks, geese, mergansers, swans, etc. Index for each volume. Bibliographies of 268 items. 106 full-page plates containing close to 200 photographs. Total of 685pp. 5⅜ x 8½.
Vol. I: T285 Paperbound **$2.50**
Vol. II: T286 Paperbound **$2.50**
The set Paperbound **$5.00**

LIFE HISTORIES OF NORTH AMERICAN GULLS AND TERNS. 50 different varieties of gulls and terns. Index. Bibliography. 93 plates including 149 photographs. xii + 337pp. 5⅜ x 8½.
T1029 Paperbound **$2.75**

LIFE HISTORIES OF NORTH AMERICAN GALLINACEOUS BIRDS. Including partridge, quail, grouse, pheasant, pigeons, doves, and others. Index. Bibliography. 93 full-page plates including 170 photographs. xiii + 490pp. 5⅜ x 8½. T1028 Paperbound **$2.75**

THE MALAY ARCHIPELAGO, Alfred Russel Wallace. The record of the explorations (8 years, 14,000 miles) of the Malay Archipelago by a great scientific observer. A contemporary of Darwin, Wallace independently arrived at the concept of evolution by natural selection, applied the new theories of evolution to later genetic discoveries, and made significant contributions to biology, zoology, and botany. This work is still one of the classics of natural history and travel. It contains the author's reports of the different native peoples of the islands, descriptions of the island groupings, his accounts of the animals, birds, and insects that flourished in this area. The reader is carried through strange lands, alien cultures, and new theories, and will share in an exciting, unrivalled travel experience. Unabridged reprint of the 1922 edition, with 62 drawings and maps. 3 appendices, one on cranial measurements. xvii + 515pp. 5⅜ x 8. T187 Paperbound **$2.00**

THE TRAVELS OF WILLIAM BARTRAM, edited by Mark Van Doren. This famous source-book of American anthropology, natural history, geography is the record kept by Bartram in the 1770's, on travels through the wilderness of Florida, Georgia, the Carolinas. Containing accurate and beautiful descriptions of Indians, settlers, fauna, flora, it is one of the finest pieces of Americana ever written. Introduction by Mark Van Doren. 13 original illustrations. Index. 448pp. 5⅜ x 8. T13 Paperbound **$2.00**

COMMON SPIDERS OF THE UNITED STATES, J. H. Emerton. Only non-technical, but thorough, reliable guide to spiders for the layman. Over 200 spiders from all parts of the country, arranged by scientific classification, are identified by shape and color, number of eyes, habitat and range, habits, etc. Full text, 501 line drawings and photographs, and valuable introduction explain webs, poisons, threads, capturing and preserving spiders, etc. Index. New synoptic key by S. W. Frost. xxiv + 225pp. 5⅜ x 8. T223 Paperbound **$1.45**

LIFE HISTORIES OF NORTH AMERICAN MARSH BIRDS. A wealth of data on 54 different kinds of marsh bird (flamingo, ibis, bittern, heron, egret, crane, crake, rail, coot, etc.). Index. Bibliography. 98 full-page plates containing 179 black-and-white photographs. xiv + 392pp. 5⅜ x 8½.   T1082 Paperbound **$2.75**

LIFE HISTORIES OF NORTH AMERICAN DIVING BIRDS. Thirty-six different diving birds including grebe, loon, auk, murre, puffin, and the like. Index. Bibliography. 55 full-page plates (92 photographs). xiv + 239pp. 5⅜ x 8½.   T1091 Paperbound **$2.75**

LIFE HISTORIES OF NORTH AMERICAN WOOD WARBLERS. Covers about 58 types. Index. Bibliography. 83 full-page plates containing 125 black-and-white photographs. xi + 734pp. of text. 5⅜ x 8½.   Vol. I: T1153 Paperbound **$2.50**
Vol. II: T1154 Paperbound **$2.50**
The set Paperbound **$5.00**

LIFE HISTORIES OF NORTH AMERICAN FLYCATCHERS, LARKS, SWALLOWS, AND THEIR ALLIES. Complete information on about 78 different varieties. Index. Bibliography. 70 full-page plates (117 photographs). xi + 555pp. of text. 5⅜ x 8½.   T1090 Paperbound **$2.75**

AMERICAN WILDLIFE, AND PLANTS: A GUIDE TO WILDLIFE FOOD HABITS, A. C. Martin, H. S. Zim, A. L. Nelson. Result of 75 years of research by U. S. Fish and Wildlife Service into food and feeding habits of more than 1,000 species of birds and mammals, their distribution in America, migratory habits, and the most important plant-animal relationships. Treats over 300 common species of birds, fur and game animals, small mammals, hoofed browsers, fish, amphibians, reptiles by group, giving data on their food, ranges, habits and economies. Also focuses on the different genera of plants that furnish food for our wildlife, animals that use them, and their value. Only thorough study of its kind in existence. "Of immense value to sportsmen, naturalists, bird students, foresters, landscape architects, botanists," NATURE. "Undoubtedly an essential handbook," SCIENTIFIC MONTHLY. Unabridged republication of 1951 edition. Over 600 illustrations, maps, etc. Classified bibliography. Index. x + 500pp. 5⅜ x 8.   T793 Paperbound **$2.50**

HOW TO KNOW THE WILD FLOWERS, Mrs. Wm. Starr Dana. A Guide to the names, haunts, and habits of wild flowers. Well-known classic of nature lore. Informative and delightful. Plants classified by color and season of their typical flowers for easy identification. Thorough coverage of more than 1,000 important flowering, berry-bearing and foliage plants of Eastern and Central United States and Canada. Complete botanical information about each important plant. Also history, uses, folklore, habitat, etc. Nomenclature modernized by C. J. Hylander. 174 full-page illustrations by Marion Satterlee. xii + 481pp. 5⅜ x 8½.
T332 Paperbound **$2.00**

HOW PLANTS GET THEIR NAMES, L. H. Bailey. Introduction to botanical nomenclature for the horticulturist and garden-lover. Discussions of Carl Linnaeus, "father of botany," and analysis of his definitions of genus and species, a brief history of the science before Linnaean systematization, a chapter on plant identification, a mine of information on the rules of nomenclature and Latin stems and word-endings used in botanical nomenclature, with pronunciation guides. An important section contains a full list of generic terms of horticultural literature and common Latin words and their English botanical applications and meanings. "Written with knowledge and authority, charm and eloquence and poetic imagination on the varied aspects of the author's specialty," New York Times. 11 illustrations. vi + 181pp. 5⅜ x 8½.   T796 Paperbound **$1.25**

THE CACTACEAE: DESCRIPTIONS AND ILLUSTRATIONS OF PLANTS OF THE CACTUS FAMILY, N. L. Britton and J. N. Rose. Definitive study of plants of the Cactus Family. The authors devoted more than 15 years of research to this monumental task and produced an exhaustive, rigorously scientific account never likely to be superseded. 3 major classifications, or tribes, are recognized, under which they arrange and describe in full detail 124 genera and 1,235 species of cactus from all over the world. Complete data on each species: leaves, flowers, seeds, fruit, distribution, growth, spines, stem structure, economic uses, etc. In addition, 125 keys facilitate identification of genera and species. For teachers and students of botany and forestry, naturalists, conservationists, and nature lovers, this is an indispensable work. Unabridged republication of second (1937) edition. First edition originally published under the auspices of the Carnegie Institution, Washington, D.C. 4 vols. bound as 2. 1279 illustrations, photographs, sketches, etc. 137 plates. Total of xxvii + 1039pp. 8 x 10¼.   T771 Clothbound, 2-volume set **$20.00**

GUIDE TO SOUTHERN TREES, Elwood S. and J. George Harrar. A handy, comprehensive 700-page manual with numerous illustrations and information on more than 350 different kinds of trees, covering the entire area south of the Mason-Dixon line from the Atlantic Ocean to the Florida Keys and western Texas. Descriptions range from the common pine, cypress, walnut, beech, and elm to such rare species as Franklinia, etc. A mine of information on leaves, flowers, twigs, bark, fruit, distribution etc. of each kind of tree. Eminently readable, written in non-technical language, it is an indispensable handbook for all lovers of the outdoors. Revised edition. Index. 81-item bibliography. Glossary. 200 full-page illustrations. ix + 709pp. 4⅝ x 6⅜.   T945 Paperbound **$2.35**

WESTERN FOREST TREES, James B. Berry. For years a standard guide to the trees of the Western United States. Covers over 70 different subspecies, ranging from the Pacific shores to western South Dakota, New Mexico, etc. Much information on range and distribution, growth habits, appearance, leaves, bark, fruit, twigs, etc. for each tree discussed, plus material on wood of the trees and its uses. Basic division (Trees with needle-like leaves, scale-like leaves, and compound, lobed or divided, and simple broadleaf trees), along with almost 100 illustrations (mostly full-size) of buds, leaves, etc., aids in easy identification of just about any tree of the area. Many subsidiary keys. Revised edition. Introduction. 12 photos. 85 illustrations by Mary E. Eaton. Index. xii + 212pp. 5⅜ x 8.
T1138 Paperbound **$1.35**

MANUAL OF THE TREES OF NORTH AMERICA (EXCLUSIVE OF MEXICO), Charles Sprague Sargent. The magnum opus of the greatest American dendrologist. Based on 44 years of original research, this monumental work is still the most comprehensive and reliable sourcebook on the subject. Includes 185 genera and 717 species of trees (and many shrubs) found in the U.S., Canada, and Alaska. 783 illustrative drawings by C. E. Faxon and Mary W. Gill. An all-encompassing lifetime reference book for students, teachers of botany and forestry, naturalists, conservationists, and all nature lovers. Includes an 11-page analytical key to genera to help the beginner locate any tree by its leaf characteristics. Within the text over 100 further keys aid in easy identification. Synopsis of families. Glossary. Index. 783 illustrations, 1 map. Total of 1 + 891pp. 5⅜ x 8.
T277 Vol. I Paperbound **$2.25**
T278 Vol. II Paperbound **$2.25**
The set **$4.50**

TREES OF THE EASTERN AND CENTRAL UNITED STATES AND CANADA, W. M. Harlow, Professor of Wood Technology, College of Forestry, State University of N. Y., Syracuse, N. Y. This middle-level text is a serious work covering more than 140 native trees and important escapes, with information on general appearance, growth habit, leaf forms, flowers, fruit, bark, and other features. Commercial use, distribution, habitat, and woodlore are also given. Keys within the text enable you to locate various species with ease. With this book you can identify at sight almost any tree you are likely to encounter; you will know which trees have edible fruit, which are suitable for house planting, and much other useful and interesting information. More than 600 photographs and figures. xiii + 288pp. 4⅝ x 6½.
T395 Paperbound **$1.35**

FRUIT KEY AND TWIG KEY TO TREES AND SHRUBS (FRUIT KEY TO NORTHEASTERN TREES, TWIG TREE TO DECIDUOUS WOODY PLANTS OF EASTERN NORTH AMERICA), W. M. Harlow. The only guides with photographs of every twig and fruit described—especially valuable to the novice. The fruit key (both deciduous trees and evergreens) has an introduction explaining seeding, organs involved, fruit types and habits. The twig key introduction treats growth and morphology. In the keys proper, identification is easy and almost automatic. This exceptional work, widely used in university courses, is especially useful for identification in winter, or from the fruit or seed only. Over 350 photos, up to 3 times natural size. Bibliography, glossary, index of common and scientific names, in each key. xvii + 125pp. 5⅝ x 8⅜.
T511 Paperbound **$1.25**

HOW TO KNOW THE FERNS, F. T. Parsons. Ferns, among our most lovely native plants, are all too little known. This modern classic of nature lore will enable the layman to identify any American fern he is likely to come across. After an introduction on the structure and life of ferns, the 57 most important ferns are fully pictured and described (arranged upon a simple identification key). Index of Latin and English names. 61 illustrations and 42 full-page plates. xiv + 215pp. 5⅜ x 8.
T740 Paperbound **$1.35**

OUR SMALL NATIVE ANIMALS: THEIR HABITS AND CARE, R. Snedigar, Curator of Reptiles, Chicago Zoological Park. An unusual nature handbook containing all the vital facts of habitat, distribution, foods, and special habits in brief life histories of 114 different species of squirrels, chipmunks, rodents, larger mammals, birds, amphibians, lizards and snakes. Liberally sprinkled with first-hand anecdotes. A wealth of information on capturing and caring for these animals: proper pens and cages, correct diet, curing diseases, special equipment required, etc. Addressed to the teacher interested in classroom demonstrations, the camp director, and to anyone who ever wanted a small animal for a pet. Revised edition, New preface. Index. 62 halftones. 14 line drawings. xviii + 296pp. 5⅜ x 8⅛.
T1022 Paperbound **$1.75**

INSECT LIFE AND INSECT NATURAL HISTORY, S. W. Frost. Unusual for emphasizing habits, social life, and ecological relations of insects, rather than more academic aspects of classification and morphology. Prof. Frost's enthusiasm and knowledge are everywhere evident as he discusses insect associations, and specialized habits like leaf-mining, leaf-rolling, and case-making, the gall insects, the boring insects, aquatic insects, etc. He examines all sorts of matters not usually covered in general works, such as: insects as human food; insect music and musicians; insect response to electric and radio waves; use of insects in art and literature. The admirably executed purpose of this book, which covers the middle ground between elementary treatment and scholarly monographs, is to excite the reader to observe for himself. Over 700 illustrations. Extensive bibliography. x + 524pp. 5⅜ x 8.
T517 Paperbound **$2.45**

Biological Sciences

AN INTRODUCTION TO GENETICS, A. H. Sturtevant and G. W. Beadle. A very thorough exposition of genetic analysis and the chromosome mechanics of higher organisms by two of the world's most renowned biologists, A. H. Sturtevant, one of the founders of modern genetics, and George Beadle, Nobel laureate in 1958. Does not concentrate on the biochemical approach, but rather more on observed data from experimental evidence and results . . . from Drosophila and other life forms. Some chapter titles: Sex chromosomes; Sex-Linkage; Autosomal Inheritance;; Chromosome Maps; Intra-Chromosomal Rearrangements; Inversions—and Incomplete Chromosomes; Translocations; Lethals; Mutations; Heterogeneous Populations; Genes and Phenotypes; The Determination and Differentiation of Sex; etc. Slightly corrected reprint of 1939 edition. New preface by Drs. Sturtevant and Beadle. 1 color plate. 126 figures. Bibliographies. Index. 391pp. 5⅜ x 8½. S306 Paperbound **$2.00**

THE GENETICAL THEORY OF NATURAL SELECTION, R. A. Fisher. 2nd revised edition of a vital reviewing of Darwin's Selection Theory in terms of particulate inheritance, by one of the great authorities on experimental and theoretical genetics. Theory is stated in mathematical form. Special features of particulate inheritance are examined: evolution of dominance, maintenance of specific variability, mimicry and sexual selection, etc. 5 chapters on man and his special circumstances as a social animal. 16 photographs. Bibliography. Index. x + 310pp. 5⅜ x 8. S466 Paperbound **$2.00**

THE ORIENTATION OF ANIMALS: KINESES, TAXES AND COMPASS REACTIONS, Gottfried S. Fraenkel and Donald L. Gunn. A basic work in the field of animal orientations. Complete, detailed survey of everything known in the subject up to 1940s, enlarged and revised to cover major developments to 1960. Analyses of simpler types of orientation are presented in Part I: kinesis, klinotaxis, tropotaxis, telotaxis, etc. Part II covers more complex reactions originating from temperature changes, gravity, chemical stimulation, etc. The two-light experiment and unilateral blinding are dealt with, as is the problem of determinism or volition in lower animals. The book has become the universally-accepted guide to all who deal with the subject—zoologists, biologists, psychologists, and the like. Second, enlarged edition, revised to 1960. Bibliography of over 500 items. 135 illustrations. Indices. xiii + 376pp. 5⅜ x 8½. T786 Paperbound **$2.25**

THE BEHAVIOUR AND SOCIAL LIFE OF HONEYBEES, C. R. Ribbands. Definitive survey of all aspects of honeybee life and behavior; completely scientific in approach, but written in interesting, everyday language that both professionals and laymen will appreciate. Basic coverage of physiology, anatomy, sensory equipment; thorough account of honeybee behavior in the field (foraging activities, nectar and pollen gathering, how individuals find their way home and back to food areas, mating habits, etc.); details of communication in various field and hive situations. An extensive treatment of activities within the hive community—food sharing, wax production, comb building, swarming, the queen, her life and relationship with the workers, etc. A must for the beekeeper, natural historian, biologist, entomologist, social scientist, et al. "An indispensable reference," J. Hambleton, BEES. "Recommended in the strongest of terms," AMERICAN SCIENTIST. 9 plates. 66 figures. Indices. 693-item bibliography. 252pp. 5⅜ x 8½. T1137 Paperbound **$2.00**

BIRD DISPLAY: AN INTRODUCTION TO THE STUDY OF BIRD PSYCHOLOGY, E. A. Armstrong. The standard work on bird display, based on extensive observation by the author and reports of other observers. This important contribution to comparative psychology covers the behavior and ceremonial rituals of hundreds of birds from gannet and heron to birds of paradise and king penguins. Chapters discuss such topics as the ceremonial of the gannet, ceremonial gaping, disablement reactions, the expression of emotions, the evolution and function of social ceremonies, social hierarchy in bird life, dances of birds and men, songs, etc. Free of technical terminology, this work will be equally interesting to psychologists and zoologists as well as bird lovers of all backgrounds. 32 photographic plates. New introduction by the author. List of scientific names of birds. Bibliography. 3-part index. 431pp. 5⅜ x 8½. T1128 Paperbound **$2.00**

THE SPECIFICITY OF SEROLOGICAL REACTIONS, Karl Landsteiner. With a Chapter on Molecular Structure and Intermolecular Forces by Linus Pauling. Dr. Landsteiner, winner of the Nobel Prize in 1930 for the discovery of the human blood groups, devoted his life to fundamental research and played a leading role in the development of immunology. This authoritative study is an account of the experiments he and his colleagues carried out on antigens and serological reactions with simple compounds. Comprehensive coverage of the basic concepts of immunolgy includes such topics as: The Serological Specificity of Proteins, Antigens, Antibodies, Artificially Conjugated Antigens, Non-Protein Cell Substances such as polysaccharides, etc., Antigen-Antibody Reactions (Toxin Neutralization, Precipitin Reactions, Agglutination, etc.). Discussions of toxins, bacterial proteins, viruses, hormones, enzymes, etc. in the context of immunological phenomena. New introduction by Dr. Merrill Chase of the Rockefeller Institute. Extensive bibliography and bibliography of author's writings. Index. xviii + 330pp. 5⅜ x 8½. S299 Paperbound **$2.00**

CULTURE METHODS FOR INVERTEBRATE ANIMALS, P. S. Galtsoff, F. E. Lutz, P. S. Welch, J. G. Needham, eds. A compendium of practical experience of hundreds of scientists and technicians, covering invertebrates from protozoa to chordata, in 313 articles on 17 phyla. Explains in great detail food, protection, environment, reproduction conditions, rearing methods, embryology, breeding seasons, schedule of development, much more. Includes at least one species of each considerable group. Half the articles are on class insecta. Introduction. 97 illustrations. Bibliography. Index. xxix + 590pp. 5⅜ x 8. S526 Paperbound **$3.00**

THE BIOLOGY OF THE LABORATORY MOUSE, edited by G. D. Snell. 1st prepared in 1941 by the staff of the Roscoe B. Jackson Memorial Laboratory, this is still the standard treatise on the mouse, assembling an enormous amount of material for which otherwise you spend hours of research. Embryology, reproduction, histology, spontaneous tumor formation, genetics of tumor transplantation, endocrine secretion & tumor formation, milk, influence & tumor formation, inbred, hybrid animals, parasites, infectious diseases, care & recording. Classified bibliography of 1122 items. 172 figures, including 128 photos. ix + 497pp. 6⅛ x 9¼. S248 Clothbound **$6.00**

MATHEMATICAL BIOPHYSICS: PHYSICO-MATHEMATICAL FOUNDATIONS OF BIOLOGY, N. Rashevsky. One of most important books in modern biology, now revised, expanded with new chapters, to include most significant recent contributions. Vol. 1: Diffusion phenomena, particularly diffusion drag forces, their effects. Old theory of cell division based on diffusion drag forces, other theoretical approaches, more exhaustively treated than ever. Theories of excitation, conduction in nerves, with formal theories plus physico-chemical theory. Vol. 2: Mathematical theories of various phenomena in central nervous system. New chapters on theory of color vision, of random nets. Principle of optimal design, extended from earlier edition. Principle of relational mapping of organisms, numerous applications. Introduces into mathematical biology such branches of math as topology, theory of sets. Index. 236 illustrations. Total of 988pp. 5⅜ x 8. S574 Vol. 1 (Books 1, 2) Paperbound **$2.50** S575 Vol. 2 (Books 3, 4) Paperbound **$2.50** 2 vol. set **$5.00**

ELEMENTS OF MATHEMATICAL BIOLOGY, A. J. Lotka. A pioneer classic, the first major attempt to apply modern mathematical techniques on a large scale to phenomena of biology, biochemistry, psychology, ecology, similar life sciences. Partial Contents: Statistical meaning of irreversibility; Evolution as redistribution; Equations of kinetics of evolving systems; Chemical, inter-species equilibrium; parameters of state; Energy transformers of nature, etc. Can be read with profit even by those having no advanced math; unsurpassed as study-reference. Formerly titled ELEMENTS OF PHYSICAL BIOLOGY. 72 figures. xxx + 460pp. 5⅜ x 8. S346 Paperbound **$2.45**

THE BIOLOGY OF THE AMPHIBIA, G. K. Noble, Late Curator of Herpetology at the Am. Mus. of Nat. Hist. Probably the most used text on amphibia, unmatched in comprehensiveness, clarity, detail. 19 chapters plus 85-page supplement cover development; heredity; life history; speciation; adaptation; sex, integument, respiratory, circulatory, digestive, muscular, nervous systems; instinct, intelligence, habits, environment, economic value, relationships, classification, etc. "Nothing comparable to it," C. H. Pope, Curator of Amphibia, Chicago Mus. of Nat. Hist. 1047 bibliographic references. 174 illustrations. 600pp. 5⅜ x 8. S206 Paperbound **$2.98**

STUDIES ON THE STRUCTURE AND DEVELOPMENT OF VERTEBRATES, E. S. Goodrich. A definitive study by the greatest modern comparative anatomist. Exceptional in its accounts of the ossicles of the ear, the separate divisions of the coelom and mammalian diaphragm, and the 5 chapters devoted to the head region. Also exhaustive morphological and phylogenetic expositions of skeleton, fins and limbs, skeletal visceral arches and labial cartilages, visceral clefts and gills, vacular, respiratory, excretory, and peripheral nervous systems, etc., from fish to the higher mammals. 754 illustrations. 69 page biographical study by C. C. Hardy. Bibliography of 1186 references. "What an undertaking . . . to write a textbook which will summarize adequately and succinctly all that has been done in the realm of Vertebrate Morphology these recent years," Journal of Anatomy. Index. Two volumes. Total 906pp. 5⅜ x 8. Two vol. set S449-50 Paperbound **$5.00**

A TREATISE ON PHYSIOLOGICAL OPTICS, H. von Helmholtz, Ed. by J. P. C. Southall. Unmatched for thoroughness, soundness, and comprehensiveness, this is still the most important work ever produced in the field of physiological optics. Revised and annotated, it contains everything known about the subject up to 1925. Beginning with a careful anatomical description of the eye, the main body of the text is divided into three general categories: The Dioptrics of the Eye (covering optical imagery, blur circles on the retina, the mechanism of accommodation, chromatic aberration, etc.); The Sensations of Vision (including stimulation of the organ of vision, simple and compound colors, the intensity and duration of light, variations of sensitivity, contrast, etc.); and The Perceptions of Vision (containing movements of the eyes, the monocular field of vision, direction, perception of depth, binocular double vision, etc.). Appendices cover later findings on optical imagery, refraction, ophthalmoscopy, and many other matters. Unabridged, corrected republication of the original English translation of the third German edition. 3 volumes bound as 2. Complete bibliography, 1911-1925. Indices. 312 illustrations. 6 full-page plates, 3 in color. Total of 1,749pp. 5⅜ x 8. Two-volume set S15, 16 Clothbound **$15.00**

CATALOGUE OF DOVER BOOKS

INTRODUCTION TO PHYSIOLOGICAL OPTICS, James P. C. Southall, former Professor of Physics in Columbia University. Readable, top-flight introduction, not only for beginning students of optics, but also for other readers—physicists, biochemists, illuminating engineers, optometrists, psychologists, etc. Comprehensive coverage of such matters as the Organ of Vision (structure of the eyeball, the retina, the dioptric system, monocular and binocular vision, adaptation, etc.); The Optical System of the Eye (reflex images in the cornea and crystalline lens, Emmetropia and Ametropia, accommodation, blur circles on retina); Eye-Glasses; Eye Defects; Movements of the Eyeball in its Socket; Rod and Cone Vision; Color Vision; and other similar topics. Index. 134 figures. x +426pp. 5⅜ x 8.   S924 Paperbound **$2.25**

LIGHT, COLOUR AND VISION, Yves LeGrand. A thorough examination of the eye as a receptor of radiant energy and as a mechanism (the retina) consisting of light-sensitive cells which absorb light of various wave lengths—probably the most complete and authoritative treatment of this subject in print. Originally prepared as a series of lectures given at the Institute of Optics in Paris, subsequently enlarged for book publication. Partial contents: Radiant Energy—concept, nature, theories, etc., Sources of Radiation—artificial and natural, the Visual Receptor, Photometric Quantities, Units, Calculations, Retinal Illumination, Trivariance of Vision, Colorimetry, Luminance Difference Thresholds, Anatomy of the Retina, Theories of Vision, Photochemistry and Electro-physiology of the Retina, etc. Appendices, Exercises, with solutions. 500-item bibliography. Authorized translation by R. Hunt, J. Walsh, F. Hunt. Index. 173 illustrations. xiii + 512pp. 5⅜ x 8½.   S979 Clothbound **$10.00**

FINGER PRINTS, PALMS AND SOLES: AN INTRODUCTION TO DERMATOGLYPHICS, Harold Cummins and Charles Midlo. An introduction in non-technical language designed to acquaint the reader with a long-neglected aspect of human biology. Although a chapter dealing with fingerprint identification and the systems of classification used by the FBI, etc. has been added especially for this edition, the main concern of the book is to show how the intricate pattern of ridges and wrinkles on our fingers have a broader significance, applicable in many areas of science and life. Some topics are: the identification of two types of twins; the resolution of doubtful cases of paternity; racial variation; inheritance; the relation of fingerprints to body measurements, blood groups, criminality, character, etc. Classification and recognition of fundamental patterns and pattern types discussed fully. 149 figures. 49 tables. 361-item bibliography. Index. xii + 319pp. 5⅝ x 8⅜.   T778 Paperbound **$1.95**

Classics and histories

ANTONY VAN LEEUWENHOEK AND HIS "LITTLE ANIMALS," edited by Clifford Dobell. First book to treat extensively, accurately, life and works (relating to protozoology, bacteriology) of first microbiologist, bacteriologist, micrologist. Includes founding papers of protozoology, bacteriology; history of Leeuwenhoek's life; discussions of his microscopes, methods, language. His writing conveys sense of an enthusiastic, naive genius, as he looks at rainwater, pepper water, vinegar, frog's skin, rotifers, etc. Extremely readable, even for non-specialists. "One of the most interesting and enlightening books I have ever read," Dr. C. C. Bass, former Dean, Tulane U. School of Medicine. Only authorized edition. 400-item bibliography. Index. 32 illust. 442pp. 5⅜ x 8.   S594 Paperbound **$2.25**

THE GROWTH OF SCIENTIFIC PHYSIOLOGY, G. J. Goodfield. A compact, superbly written account of how certain scientific investigations brought about the emergence of the distinct science of physiology. Centers principally around the mechanist-vitalist controversy prior to the development of physiology as an independent science, using the arguments which raged around the problem of animal heat as its chief illustration. Covers thoroughly the efforts of clinicians and naturalists and workers in chemistry and physics to solve these problems—from which the new discipline arose. Includes the theories and contributions of: Aristotle, Galen, Harvey, Boyle, Bernard, Benjamin Franklin, Palmer, Gay-Lussac, Priestley, Spallanzani, and many others. 1960 publication. Biographical bibliography. 174pp. 5 x 7½.   T1066 Clothbound **$3.00**

MICROGRAPHIA, Robert Hooke. Hooke, 17th century British universal scientific genius, was a major pioneer in celestial mechanics, optics, gravity, and many other fields, but his greatest contribution was this book, now reprinted entirely from the original 1665 edition, which gave microscopy its first great impetus. With all the freshness of discovery, he describes fully his microscope, and his observations of cork, the edge of a razor, insects' eyes, fabrics, and dozens of other different objects. 38 plates, full-size or larger, contain all the original illustrations. This book is also a fundamental classic in the fields of combustion and heat theory, light and color theory, botany and zoology, hygrometry, and many other fields. It contains such farsighted predictions as the famous anticipation of artificial silk. The final section is concerned with Hooke's telescopic observations of the moon and stars. 323pp. 5⅜ x 8.   T8 Paperbound **$2.00**

Art, History of Art, Antiques, Graphic Arts, Handcrafts

ART STUDENTS' ANATOMY, E. J. Farris. Outstanding art anatomy that uses chiefly living objects for its illustrations. 71 photos of undraped men, women, children are accompanied by carefully labeled matching sketches to illustrate the skeletal system, articulations and movements, bony landmarks, the muscular system, skin, fasciae, fat, etc. 9 x-ray photos show movement of joints. Undraped models are shown in such actions as serving in tennis, drawing a bow in archery, playing football, dancing, preparing to spring and to dive. Also discussed and illustrated are proportions, age and sex differences, the anatomy of the smile, etc. 8 plates by the great early 18th century anatomic illustrator Siegfried Albinus are also included. Glossary. 158 figures, 7 in color. x + 159pp. 5⅝ x 8⅜.　　　　T744 Paperbound **$1.50**

AN ATLAS OF ANATOMY FOR ARTISTS, F Schider. A new 3rd edition of this standard text enlarged by 52 new illustrations of hands, anatomical studies by Cloquet, and expressive life studies of the body by Barcsay. 189 clear, detailed plates offer you precise information of impeccable accuracy. 29 plates show all aspects of the skeleton, with closeups of special areas, while 54 full-page plates, mostly in two colors, give human musculature as seen from four different points of view, with cutaways for important portions of the body. 14 full-page plates provide photographs of hand forms, eyelids, female breasts, and indicate the location of muscles upon models. 59 additional plates show how great artists of the past utilized human anatomy. They reproduce sketches and finished work by such artists as Michelangelo, Leonardo da Vinci, Goya, and 15 others. This is a lifetime reference work which will be one of the most important books in any artist's library. "The standard reference tool," AMERICAN LIBRARY ASSOCIATION. "Excellent," AMERICAN ARTIST. Third enlarged edition. 189 plates, 647 illustrations. xxvi + 192pp. 7⅞ x 10⅝.　　　T241 Clothbound **$6.00**

AN ATLAS OF ANIMAL ANATOMY FOR ARTISTS, W. Ellenberger, H. Baum, H. Dittrich. The largest, richest animal anatomy for artists available in English. 99 detailed anatomical plates of such animals as the horse, dog, cat, lion, deer, seal, kangaroo, flying squirrel, cow, bull, goat, monkey, hare, and bat. Surface features are clearly indicated, while progressive beneath-the-skin pictures show musculature, tendons, and bone structure. Rest and action are exhibited in terms of musculature and skeletal structure and detailed cross-sections are given for heads and important features. The animals chosen are representative of specific families so that a study of these anatomies will provide knowledge of hundreds of related species. "Highly recommended as one of the very few books on the subject worthy of being used as an authoritative guide," DESIGN. "Gives a fundamental knowledge," AMERICAN ARTIST. Second revised, enlarged edition with new plates from Cuvier, Stubbs, etc. 288 illustrations. 153pp. 11⅜ x 9.　　　　T82 Clothbound **$6.00**

THE HUMAN FIGURE IN MOTION, Eadweard Muybridge. The largest selection in print of Muybridge's famous high-speed action photos of the human figure in motion. 4789 photographs illustrate 162 different actions: men, women, children—mostly undraped—are shown walking, running, carrying various objects, sitting, lying down, climbing, throwing, arising, and performing over 150 other actions. Some actions are shown in as many as 150 photographs each. All in all there are more than 500 action strips in this enormous volume, series shots taken at shutter speeds of as high as 1/6000th of a second! These are not posed shots, but true stopped motion. They show bone and muscle in situations that the human eye is not fast enough to capture. Earlier, smaller editions of these prints have brought $40 and more on the out-of-print market. "A must for artists," ART IN FOCUS. "An unparalleled dictionary of action for all artists," AMERICAN ARTIST. 390 full-page plates, with 4789 photographs. Printed on heavy glossy stock. Reinforced binding with headbands. xxi + 390pp. 7⅞ x 10⅝.
　　　　　　　　　　　　　　　　　　　　　　　　　　　T204 Clothbound **$10.00**

ANIMALS IN MOTION, Eadweard Muybridge. This is the largest collection of animal action photos in print. 34 different animals (horses, mules, oxen, goats, camels, pigs, cats, guanacos, lions, gnus, deer, monkeys, eagles—and 21 others) in 132 characteristic actions. The horse alone is shown in more than 40 different actions. All 3919 photographs are taken in series at speeds up to 1/6000th of a second. The secrets of leg motion, spinal patterns, head movements, strains and contortions shown nowhere else are captured. You will see exactly how a lion sets his foot down; how an elephant's knees are like a human's—and how they differ; the position of a kangaroo's legs in mid-leap; how an ostrich's head bobs; details of the flight of birds—and thousands of facets of motion only the fastest cameras can catch. Photographed from domestic animals and animals in the Philadelphia zoo, it contains neither semiposed artificial shots nor distorted telephoto shots taken under adverse conditions. Artists, biologists, decorators, cartoonists, will find this book indispensable for understanding animals in motion. "A really marvelous series of plates," NATURE (London). "The dry plate's most spectacular early use was by Eadweard Muybridge," LIFE. 3919 photographs; 380 full pages of plates. 440pp. Printed on heavy glossy paper. Deluxe binding with headbands. 7⅞ x 10⅝.　　　　　　　　　　　　　　　　　　　T203 Clothbound **$10.00**

THE AUTOBIOGRAPHY OF AN IDEA, Louis Sullivan. The pioneer architect whom Frank Lloyd Wright called "the master" reveals an acute sensitivity to social forces and values in this passionately honest account. He records the crystallization of his opinions and theories, the growth of his organic theory of architecture that still influences American designers and architects, contemporary ideas, etc. This volume contains the first appearance of 34 full-page plates of his finest architecture. Unabridged reissue of 1924 edition. New introduction by R. M. Line. Index. xiv + 335pp. 5⅜ x 8.   T281 Paperbound **$2.00**

THE DRAWINGS OF HEINRICH KLEY. The first uncut republication of both of Kley's devastating sketchbooks, which first appeared in pre-World War I Germany. One of the greatest cartoonists and social satirists of modern times, his exuberant and iconoclastic fantasy and his extraordinary technique place him in the great tradition of Bosch, Breughel, and Goya, while his subject matter has all the immediacy and tension of our century. 200 drawings. viii + 128pp. 7¾ x 10¾.   T24 Paperbound **$1.85**

MORE DRAWINGS BY HEINRICH KLEY. All the sketches from Leut' Und Viecher (1912) and Sammel-Album (1923) not included in the previous Dover edition of Drawings. More of the bizarre, mercilessly iconoclastic sketches that shocked and amused on their original publication. Nothing was too sacred, no one too eminent for satirization by this imaginative, individual and accomplished master cartoonist. A total of 158 illustrations. Iv + 104pp. 7¾ x 10¾.   T41 Paperbound **$1.85**

PINE FURNITURE OF EARLY NEW ENGLAND, R. H. Kettell. A rich understanding of one of America's most original folk arts that collectors of antiques, interior decorators, craftsmen, woodworkers, and everyone interested in American history and art will find fascinating and immensely useful. 413 illustrations of more than 300 chairs, benches, racks, beds, cupboards, mirrors, shelves, tables, and other furniture will show all the simple beauty and character of early New England furniture. 55 detailed drawings carefully analyze outstanding pieces. "With its rich store of illustrations, this book emphasizes the individuality and varied design of early American pine furniture. It should be welcomed," ANTIQUES. 413 illustrations and 55 working drawings. 475. 8 x 10¾.   T145 Clothbound **$10.00**

THE HUMAN FIGURE, J. H. Vanderpoel. Every important artistic element of the human figure is pointed out in minutely detailed word descriptions in this classic text and illustrated as well in 430 pencil and charcoal drawings. Thus the text of this book directs your attention to all the characteristic features and subtle differences of the male and female (adults, children, and aged persons), as though a master artist were telling you what to look for at each stage. 2nd edition, revised and enlarged by George Bridgman. Foreword. 430 illustrations. 143pp. 6⅛ x 9¼.   T432 Paperbound **$1.50**

LETTERING AND ALPHABETS, J. A. Cavanagh. This unabridged reissue of LETTERING offers a full discussion, analysis, illustration of 89 basic hand lettering styles — styles derived from Caslons, Bodonis, Garamonds, Gothic, Black Letter, Oriental, and many others. Upper and lower cases, numerals and common signs pictured. Hundreds of technical hints on make-up, construction, artistic validity, strokes, pens, brushes, white areas, etc. May be reproduced without permission! 89 complete alphabets; 72 lettered specimens. 121pp. 9¾ x 8.   T53 Paperbound **$1.35**

STICKS AND STONES, Lewis Mumford. A survey of the forces that have conditioned American architecture and altered its forms. The author discusses the medieval tradition in early New England villages; the Renaissance influence which developed with the rise of the merchant class; the classical influence of Jefferson's time; the "Mechanicsvilles" of Poe's generation; the Brown Decades; the philosophy of the Imperial facade; and finally the modern machine age. "A truly remarkable book," SAT. REV. OF LITERATURE. 2nd revised edition. 21 illustrations. xvii + 228pp. 5⅜ x 8.   T202 Paperbound **$1.65**

THE STANDARD BOOK OF QUILT MAKING AND COLLECTING, Marguerite Ickis. A complete easy-to-follow guide with all the information you need to make beautiful, useful quilts. How to plan, design, cut, sew, appliqué, avoid sewing problems, use rag bag, make borders, tuft, every other aspect. Over 100 traditional quilts shown, including over 40 full-size patterns. At-home hobby for fun, profit. Index. 483 illus. 1 color plate. 287pp. 6¾ x 9½.   T582 Paperbound **$2.00**

THE BOOK OF SIGNS, Rudolf Koch. Formerly $20 to $25 on the out-of-print market, now only $1.00 in this unabridged new edition! 493 symbols from ancient manuscripts, medieval cathedrals, coins, catacombs, pottery, etc. Crosses, monograms of Roman emperors, astrological, chemical, botanical, runes, housemarks, and 7 other categories. Invaluable for handicraft workers, illustrators, scholars, etc., this material may be reproduced without permission. 493 illustrations by Fritz Kredel. 104pp. 6½ x 9¼.   T162 Paperbound **$1.00**

PRIMITIVE ART, Franz Boas. This authoritative and exhaustive work by a great American anthropologist covers the entire gamut of primitive art. Pottery, leatherwork, metal work, stone work, wood, basketry, are treated in detail. Theories of primitive art, historical depth in art history, technical virtuosity, unconscious levels of patterning, symbolism, styles, literature, music, dance, etc. A must book for the interested layman, the anthropologist, artist, handicrafter (hundreds of unusual motifs), and the historian. Over 900 illustrations (50 ceramic vessels, 12 totem poles, etc.). 376pp. 5⅜ x 8.   T25 Paperbound **$2.00**

Psychology

YOGA: A SCIENTIFIC EVALUATION, Kovoor T. Behanan. A complete reprinting of the book that for the first time gave Western readers a sane, scientific explanation and analysis of yoga. The author draws on controlled laboratory experiments and personal records of a year as a disciple of a yoga, to investigate yoga psychology, concepts of knowledge, physiology, "supernatural" phenomena, and the ability to tap the deepest human powers. In this study under the auspices of Yale University Institute of Human Relations, the strictest principles of physiological and psychological inquiry are followed throughout. Foreword by W. A. Miles, Yale University. 17 photographs. Glossary. Index. xx + 270pp. 5⅜ x 8. T505 Paperbound **$2.00**

CONDITIONED REFLEXES: AN INVESTIGATION OF THE PHYSIOLOGICAL ACTIVITIES OF THE CEREBRAL CORTEX, I. P. Pavlov. Full, authorized translation of Pavlov's own survey of his work in experimental psychology reviews entire course of experiments, summarizes conclusions, outlines psychological system based on famous "conditioned reflex" concept. Details of technical means used in experiments, observations on formation of conditioned reflexes, function of cerebral hemispheres, results of damage, nature of sleep, typology of nervous system, significance of experiments for human psychology. Trans. by Dr. G. V. Anrep, Cambridge Univ. 235-item bibliography. 18 figures. 445pp. 5⅜ x 8. S614 Paperbound **$2.35**

EXPLANATION OF HUMAN BEHAVIOUR, F. V. Smith. A major intermediate-level introduction to and criticism of 8 complete systems of the psychology of human behavior, with unusual emphasis on theory of investigation and methodology. Part I is an illuminating analysis of the problems involved in the explanation of observed phenomena, and the differing viewpoints on the nature of causality. Parts II and III are a closely detailed survey of the systems of McDougall, Gordon Allport, Lewin, the Gestalt group, Freud, Watson, Hull, and Tolman. Biographical notes. Bibliography of over 800 items. 2 Indexes. 38 figures. xii + 460pp. 5½ x 8¾. T253 Clothbound **$6.00**

SEX IN PSYCHO-ANALYSIS (formerly CONTRIBUTIONS TO PSYCHO-ANALYSIS), S. Ferenczi. Written by an associate of Freud, this volume presents countless insights on such topics as impotence, transference, analysis and children, dreams, symbols, obscene words, masturbation and male homosexuality, paranoia and psycho-analysis, the sense of reality, hypnotism and therapy, and many others. Also includes full text of THE DEVELOPMENT OF PSYCHO-ANALYSIS by Ferenczi and Otto Rank. Two books bound as one. Total of 406pp. 5⅜ x 8. T324 Paperbound **$1.85**

BEYOND PSYCHOLOGY, Otto Rank. One of Rank's most mature contributions, focussing on the irrational basis of human behavior as a basic fact of our lives. The psychoanalytic techniques of myth analysis trace to their source the ultimates of human existence: fear of death, personality, the social organization, the need for love and creativity, etc. Dr. Rank finds them stemming from a common irrational source, man's fear of final destruction. A seminal work in modern psychology, this work sheds light on areas ranging from the concept of immortal soul to the sources of state power. 291pp. 5⅜ x 8. T485 Paperbound **$2.00**

ILLUSIONS AND DELUSIONS OF THE SUPERNATURAL AND THE OCCULT, D. H. Rawcliffe. Holds up to rational examination hundreds of persistent delusions including crystal gazing, automatic writing, table turning, mediumistic trances, mental healing, stigmata, lycanthropy, live burial, the Indian Rope Trick, spiritualism, dowsing, telepathy, clairvoyance, ghosts, ESP, etc. The author explains and exposes the mental and physical deceptions involved, making this not only an exposé of supernatural phenomena, but a valuable exposition of characteristic types of abnormal psychology. Originally titled "The Psychology of the Occult." 14 illustrations. Index. 551pp. 5⅜ x 8. T503 Paperbound **$2.00**

THE PRINCIPLES OF PSYCHOLOGY, William James. The full long-course, unabridged, of one of the great classics of Western literature and science. Wonderfully lucid descriptions of human mental activity, the stream of thought, consciousness, time perception, memory, imagination, emotions, reason, abnormal phenomena, and similar topics. Original contributions are integrated with the work of such men as Berkeley, Binet, Mills, Darwin, Hume, Kant, Royce, Schopenhauer, Spinoza, Locke, Descartes, Galton, Wundt, Lotze, Herbart, Fechner, and scores of others. All contrasting interpretations of mental phenomena are examined in detail — introspective analysis, philosophical interpretation, and experimental research. "A classic," JOURNAL OF CONSULTING PSYCHOLOGY. "The main lines are as valid as ever," PSYCHO-ANALYTICAL QUARTERLY. "Standard reading . . . a classic of interpretation," PSYCHIATRIC QUARTERLY. 94 illustrations. 1408pp. 2 volumes. 5⅜ x 8. Vol. 1, T381 Paperbound **$2.50**
Vol. 2, T382 Paperbound **$2.50**

THE DYNAMICS OF THERAPY IN A CONTROLLED RELATIONSHIP, Jessie Taft. One of the most important works in literature of child psychology, out of print for 25 years. Outstanding disciple of Rank describes all aspects of relationship or Rankian therapy through concise, simple elucidation of theory underlying her actual contacts with two seven-year olds. Therapists, social caseworkers, psychologists, counselors, and laymen who work with children will all find this important work an invaluable summation of method, theory of child psychology. xix + 296pp. 5⅜ x 8. T325 Paperbound **$1.75**

Dover Classical Records

Now available directly to the public exclusively from Dover: top-quality recordings of fine classical music for only $2 per record! Originally released by a major company (except for the previously unreleased Gimpel recording of Bach) to sell for $5 and $6, these records were issued under our imprint only after they had passed a severe critical test. We insisted upon:

First-rate music that is enjoyable, musically important and culturally significant.

First-rate performances, where the artists have carried out the composer's intentions, in which the music is alive, vigorous, played with understanding and sympathy.

First-rate sound—clear, sonorous, fully balanced, crackle-free, whir-free.

Have in your home music by major composers, performed by such gifted musicians as Elsner, Gitlis, Wührer, the Barchet Quartet, Gimpel. Enthusiastically received when first released, many of these performances are definitive. The records are not seconds or remainders, but brand new pressings made on pure vinyl from carefully chosen master tapes. "All purpose" 12" monaural 33⅓ rpm records, they play equally well on hi-fi and stereo equipment. Fine music for discriminating music lovers, superlatively played, flawlessly recorded: there is no better way to build your library of recorded classical music at remarkable savings. There are no strings; this is not a come-on, not a club, forcing you to buy records you may not want in order to get a few at a lower price. Buy whatever records you want in any quantity, and never pay more than $2 each. Your obligation ends with your first purchase. And that's when ours begins. Dover's money-back guarantee allows you to return any record for any reason, even if you don't like the music, for a full, immediate refund, no questions asked.

MOZART: STRING QUARTET IN A MAJOR (K.464); STRING QUARTET IN C MAJOR ("DISSONANT", K.465), Barchet Quartet. The final two of the famed Haydn Quartets, high-points in the history of music. The A Major was accepted with delight by Mozart's contemporaries, but the C Major, with its dissonant opening, aroused strong protest. Today, of course, the remarkable resolutions of the dissonances are recognized as major musical achievements. "Beautiful warm playing," MUSICAL AMERICA. "Two of Mozart's loveliest quartets in a distinguished performance," REV. OF RECORDED MUSIC. (Playing time 58 mins.) HCR 5200 **$2.00**

MOZART: QUARTETS IN G MAJOR (K.80); D MAJOR (K.155); G MAJOR (K.156); C MAJOR (K157), Barchet Quartet. The early chamber music of Mozart receives unfortunately little attention. First-rate music of the Italian school, it contains all the lightness and charm that belongs only to the youthful Mozart. This is currently the only separate source for the composer's work of this time period. "Excellent," HIGH FIDELITY. "Filled with sunshine and youthful joy; played with verve, recorded sound live and brilliant," CHRISTIAN SCI. MONITOR. (Playing time 51 mins.) HCR 5201 **$2.00**

MOZART: SERENADE #9 IN D MAJOR ("POSTHORN", K.320); SERENADE #6 IN D MAJOR ("SERENATA NOTTURNA", K.239), Pro Musica Orch. of Stuttgart, under Edouard van Remoortel. For Mozart, the serenade was a highly effective form, since he could bring to it the immediacy and intimacy of chamber music as well as the free fantasy of larger group music. Both these serenades are distinguished by a playful, mischievous quality, a spirit perfectly captured in this fine performance. "A triumph, polished playing from the orchestra," HI FI MUSIC AT HOME. "Sound is rich and resonant, fidelity is wonderful," REV. OF RECORDED MUSIC. (Playing time 51 mins.) HCR 5202 **$2.00**

MOZART: DIVERTIMENTO IN E FLAT MAJOR FOR STRING TRIO (K.563); ADAGIO AND FUGUE IN F MINOR FOR STRING TRIO (K.404a), Kehr Trio. The Divertimento is one of Mozart's most beloved pieces, called by Einstein "the finest, most perfect trio ever heard." It is difficult to imagine a music lover who will not be delighted by it. This is the only recording of the lesser known Adagio and Fugue, written in 1782 and influenced by Bach's Well-Tempered Clavichord. "Extremely beautiful recording, strongly recommended," THE OBSERVER. "Superior to rival editions," HIGH FIDELITY. (Playing time 51 mins.) HCR 5203 **$2.00**

SCHUMANN: KREISLERIANA (OP.16); FANTASY IN C MAJOR ("FANTASIE," OP.17), Vlado Perlemuter, Piano. The vigorous Romantic imagination and the remarkable emotional qualities of Schumann's piano music raise it to special eminence in 19th century creativity. Both these pieces are rooted to the composer's tortuous romance with his future wife, Clara, and both receive brilliant treatment at the hands of Vlado Perlemuter, Paris Conservatory, proclaimed by Alfred Cortot "not only a great virtuoso but also a great musician." "The best Kreisleriana to date," BILLBOARD. (Playing time 55 mins.) HCR 5204 **$2.00**

SCHUMANN: TRIO #1, D MINOR; TRIO #3, G MINOR, Trio di Bolzano. The fiery, romantic, melodic Trio #1, and the dramatic, seldom heard Trio #3 are both movingly played by a fine chamber ensemble. No one personified Romanticism to the general public of the 1840's more than did Robert Schumann, and among his most romantic works are these trios for cello, violin and piano. "Ensemble and overall interpretation leave little to be desired," HIGH FIDELITY. "An especially understanding performance," REV. OF RECORDED MUSIC. (Playing time 54 mins.) HCR 5205 **$2.00**

Philosophy, Religion

GUIDE TO PHILOSOPHY, C. E. M. Joad. A modern classic which examines many crucial problems which man has pondered through the ages: Does free will exist? Is there plan in the universe? How do we know and validate our knowledge? Such opposed solutions as subjective idealism and realism, chance and teleology, vitalism and logical positivism, are evaluated and the contributions of the great philosophers from the Greeks to moderns like Russell, Whitehead, and others, are considered in the context of each problem. "The finest introduction," BOSTON TRANSCRIPT. Index. Classified bibliography. 592pp. 5⅜ x 8.
T297 Paperbound **$2.00**

HISTORY OF ANCIENT PHILOSOPHY, W. Windelband. One of the clearest, most accurate comprehensive surveys of Greek and Roman philosophy. Discusses ancient philosophy in general, intellectual life in Greece in the 7th and 6th centuries B.C., Thales, Anaximander, Anaximenes, Heraclitus, the Eleatics, Empedocles, Anaxagoras, Leucippus, the Pythagoreans, the Sophists, Socrates, Democritus (20 pages), Plato (50 pages), Aristotle (70 pages), the Peripatetics, Stoics, Epicureans, Sceptics, Neo-platonists, Christian Apologists, etc. 2nd German edition translated by H. E. Cushman. xv + 393pp. 5⅜ x 8.
T357 Paperbound **$1.85**

ILLUSTRATIONS OF THE HISTORY OF MEDIEVAL THOUGHT AND LEARNING, R. L. Poole. Basic analysis of the thought and lives of the leading philosophers and ecclesiastics from the 8th to the 14th century—Abailard, Ockham, Wycliffe, Marsiglio of Padua, and many other great thinkers who carried the torch of Western culture and learning through the "Dark Ages": political, religious, and metaphysical views. Long a standard work for scholars and one of the best introductions to medieval thought for beginners. Index. 10 Appendices. xiii + 327pp. 5⅜ x 8.
T674 Paperbound **$2.00**

PHILOSOPHY AND CIVILIZATION IN THE MIDDLE AGES, M. de Wulf. This semi-popular survey covers aspects of medieval intellectual life such as religion, philosophy, science, the arts, etc. It also covers feudalism vs. Catholicism, rise of the universities, mendicant orders, monastic centers, and similar topics. Unabridged. Bibliography. Index. viii + 320pp. 5⅜ x 8.
T284 Paperbound **$1.85**

AN INTRODUCTION TO SCHOLASTIC PHILOSOPHY, Prof. M. de Wulf. Formerly entitled SCHOLASTICISM OLD AND NEW, this volume examines the central scholastic tradition from St. Anselm, Albertus Magnus, Thomas Aquinas, up to Suarez in the 17th century. The relation of scholasticism to ancient and medieval philosophy and science in general is clear and easily followed. The second part of the book considers the modern revival of scholasticism, the Louvain position, relations with Kantianism and Positivism. Unabridged. xvi + 271pp. 5⅜ x 8.
T296 Clothbound **$3.50**
T283 Paperbound **$1.75**

A HISTORY OF MODERN PHILOSOPHY, H. Höffding. An exceptionally clear and detailed coverage of western philosophy from the Renaissance to the end of the 19th century. Major and minor men such as Pomponazzi, Bodin, Boehme, Telesius, Bruno, Copernicus, da Vinci, Kepler, Galileo, Bacon, Descartes, Hobbes, Spinoza, Leibniz, Wolff, Locke, Newton, Berkeley, Hume, Erasmus, Montesquieu, Voltaire, Diderot, Rousseau, Lessing, Kant, Herder, Fichte, Schelling, Hegel, Schopenhauer, Comte, Mill, Darwin, Spencer, Hartmann, Lange, and many others, are discussed in terms of theory of knowledge, logic, cosmology, and psychology. Index. 2 volumes, total of 1159pp. 5⅜ x 8.
T117 Vol. 1, Paperbound **$2.25**
T118 Vol. 2, Paperbound **$2.25**

ARISTOTLE, A. E. Taylor. A brilliant, searching non-technical account of Aristotle and his thought written by a foremost Platonist. It covers the life and works of Aristotle; classification of the sciences; logic; first philosophy; matter and form; causes; motion and eternity; God; physics; metaphysics; and similar topics. Bibliography. New Index compiled for this edition. 128pp. 5⅜ x 8.
T280 Paperbound **$1.00**

THE SYSTEM OF THOMAS AQUINAS, M. de Wulf. Leading Neo-Thomist, one of founders of University of Louvain, gives concise exposition to central doctrines of Aquinas, as a means toward determining his value to modern philosophy, religion. Formerly "Medieval Philosophy Illustrated from the System of Thomas Aquinas." Trans. by E. Messenger. Introduction. 151pp. 5⅜ x 8.
T568 Paperbound **$1.25**

LEIBNIZ, H. W. Carr. Most stimulating middle-level coverage of basic philosophical thought of Leibniz. Easily understood discussion, analysis of major works: "Theodicy," "Principles of Nature and Grace," "Monadology"; Leibniz's influence; Intellectual growth; correspondence; disputes with Bayle, Malebranche, Newton; importance of his thought today, with reinterpretation in modern terminology. "Power and mastery," London Times. Bibliography. Index. 226pp. 5⅜ x 8.
T624 Paperbound **$1.35**

New Books

101 PATCHWORK PATTERNS, Ruby Short McKim. With no more ability than the fundamentals of ordinary sewing, you will learn to make over 100 beautiful quilts: flowers, rainbows, Irish chains, fish and bird designs, leaf designs, unusual geometric patterns, many others. Cutting designs carefully diagrammed and described, suggestions for materials, yardage estimates, step-by-step instructions, plus entertaining stories of origins of quilt names, other folklore. Revised 1962. 101 full-sized patterns. 140 illustrations. Index. 128pp. 7⅞ x 10¾.
T773 Paperbound **$1.85**

ESSENTIAL GRAMMAR SERIES
By concentrating on the essential core of material that constitutes the semantically most important forms and areas of a language and by stressing explanation (often bringing parallel English forms into the discussion) rather than rote memory, this new series of grammar books is among the handiest language aids ever devised. Designed by linguists and teachers for adults with limited learning objectives and learning time, these books omit nothing important, yet they teach more usable language material and do it more quickly and permanently than any other self-study material. Clear and rigidly economical, they concentrate upon immediately usable language material, logically organized so that related material is always presented together. Any reader of typical capability can use them to refresh his grasp of language, to supplement self-study language records or conventional grammars used in schools, or to begin language study on his own. Now available:

ESSENTIAL GERMAN GRAMMAR, Dr. Guy Stern & E. F. Bleiler. Index. Glossary of terms. 128pp. 5⅜ x 8.
T422 Paperbound **$1.00**

ESSENTIAL FRENCH GRAMMAR, Dr. Seymour Resnick. Index. Cognate list. Glossary. 159pp. 5⅜ x 8.
T419 Paperbound **$1.00**

ESSENTIAL ITALIAN GRAMMAR, Dr. Olga Ragusa. Index. Glossary. 111pp. 5⅜ x 8.
T779 Paperbound · **$1.00**

ESSENTIAL SPANISH GRAMMAR, Dr. Seymour Resnick. Index. 50-page cognate list. Glossary. 138pp. 5⅜ x 8.
T780 Paperbound **$1.00**

PHILOSOPHIES OF MUSIC HISTORY: A Study of General Histories of Music, 1600-1960, Warren D. Allen. Unquestionably one of the most significant documents yet to appear in musicology, this thorough survey covers the entire field of historical research in music. An influential masterpiece of scholarship, it includes early music histories; theories on the ethos of music; lexicons, dictionaries and encyclopedias of music; musical historiography through the centuries; philosophies of music history; scores of related topics. Copiously documented. New preface brings work up to 1960. Index. 317-item bibliography. 9 illustrations; 3 full-page plates. 5⅜ x 8½. xxxiv + 382pp.
T282 Paperbound **$2.00**

MR. DOOLEY ON IVRYTHING AND IVRYBODY, Finley Peter Dunne. The largest collection in print of hilarious utterances by the irrepressible Irishman of Archey Street, one of the most vital characters in American fiction. Gathered from the half dozen books that appeared during the height of Mr. Dooley's popularity, these 102 pieces are all unaltered and uncut, and they are all remarkably fresh and pertinent even today. Selected and edited by Robert Hutchinson. 5⅜ x 8½. xii + 244p.
T626 Paperbound **$1.00**

TREATISE ON PHYSIOLOGICAL OPTICS, Hermann von Helmholtz. Despite new investigations, this important work will probably remain preeminent. Contains everything known about physiological optics up to 1925, covering scores of topics under the general headings of dioptrics of the eye, sensations of vision, and pereeptions of vision. Von Helmholtz's voluminous data are all included, as are extensive supplementary matter incorporated into the third German edition, new material prepared for 1925 English edition, and copious textual annotations by J. P. C. Southall. The most exhaustive treatise ever prepared on the subject, it has behind it a list of contributors that will never again be duplicated. Translated and edited by J. P. C. Southall. Bibliography. Indexes. 312 illustrations. 3 volumes bound as 2. Total of 1749pp. 5⅜ x 8.
S15-16 Two volume set, Clothbound **$15.00**

THE ARTISTIC ANATOMY OF TREES, Rex Vicat Cole. Even the novice with but an elementary knowledge of drawing and none of the structure of trees can learn to draw, paint trees from this systematic, lucid instruction book. Copiously illustrated with the author's own sketches, diagrams, and 50 paintings from the early Renaissance to today, it covers composition; structure of twigs, boughs, buds, branch systems; outline forms of major species; how leaf is set on twig; flowers and fruit and their arrangement; etc. 500 illustrations. Bibliography. Indexes. 347pp. 5⅜ x 8.
T1016 Clothbound **$4.50**

HOW PLANTS GET THEIR NAMES, L. H. Bailey. In this basic introduction to botanical nomenclature, a famed expert on plants and plant life reveals the confusion that can result from misleading common names of plants and points out the fun and advantage of using a sound, scientific approach. Covers every aspect of the subject, including an historical survey beginning before Linnaeus systematized nomenclature, the literal meaning of scores of Latin names, their English equivalents, etc. Enthusiastically written and easy to follow, this handbook for gardeners, amateur horticulturalists, and beginning botany students is knowledgeable, accurate and useful. 11 illustrations. Lists of Latin, English botanical names. 192pp. 5⅜ x 8½.
T796 Paperbound **$1.15**

PIERRE CURIE, Marie Curie. Nobel Prize winner creates a memorable portrait of her equally famous husband in a fine scientific biography. Recounting his childhood, his haphazard education, and his experimental research (with his brother) in the physics of crystals, Mme. Curie brings to life the strong, determined personality of a great scientist at work and discusses, in clear, straightforward terms, her husband's and her own work with radium and radioactivity. A great book about two very great founders of modern science. Includes Mme. Curie's autobiographical notes. Translated by Charlotte and Vernon Kellogg. viii + 120pp. 5⅜ x 8½.
T199 Paperbound **$1.00**

STYLES IN PAINTING: A Comparative Study, Paul Zucker. Professor of Art History at Cooper Union presents an important work of art-understanding that will guide you to a fuller, deeper appreciation of masterpieces of art and at the same time add to your understanding of how they fit into the evolution of style from the earliest times to this century. Discusses general principles of historical method and aesthetics, history of styles, then illustrates with more than 230 great paintings organized by subject matter so you can see at a glance how styles have changed through the centuries. 236 beautiful halftones. xiv + 338pp. 5⅝ x 8½.
T760 Paperbound **$2.00**

NEW VARIORUM EDITION OF SHAKESPEARE
One of the monumental feats of Shakespeare scholarship is the famous New Variorum edition, containing full texts of the plays together with an entire reference library worth of historical and critical information: all the variant readings that appear in the quartos and folios; annotations by leading scholars from the earliest days of Shakespeare criticism to the date of publication; essays on meaning, background, productions by Johnson, Addison, Fielding, Lessing, Hazlitt, Coleridge, Ulrici, Swinburne, and other major Shakespeare critics; original sources of Shakespeare's inspiration. For the first time, this definitive edition of Shakespeare's plays, each printed in a separate volume, will be available in inexpensive editions to scholars, to teachers and students, and to every lover of Shakespeare and fine literature. Now ready:

KING LEAR, edited by Horace Howard Furness. Bibliography. List of editions collated in notes. viii + 503pp. 5⅜ x 8½.
T1000 Paperbound **$2.25**

MACBETH, edited by Horace Howard Furness Jr. Bibliography. List of editions collated in notes. xvi + 562pp. 5⅜ x 8½.
T1001 Paperbound **$2.25**

ROMEO AND JULIET, edited by Horace Howard Furness. Bibliography. List of editions collated in notes. xxvi + 480pp. 5⅜ x 8½.
T1002 Paperbound **$2.25**

OTTHELLO, edited by Horace Howard Furness. Bibliography. List of editions collated in notes. x + 471pp. 5⅜ x 8½.
T1003 Paperbound **$2.25**

HAMLET, edited by Horace Howard Furness. Bibliography. List of editions collated in notes. Total of 926pp. 5⅜ x 8½.
T1004-1005 Two volume set, Paperbound **$4.50**

THE GARDENER'S YEAR, Karel Capek. The author of this refreshingly funny book is probably best known in U. S. as the author of "R. U. R.," a biting satire on the machine age. Here, his satiric genius finds expression in a wholly different vein: a warm, witty chronicle of the joys and trials of the amateur gardener as he watches over his plants, his soil and the weather from January to December. 59 drawings by Joseph Capek add an important second dimension to the fun. "Mr. Capek writes with sympathy, understanding and humor," NEW YORK TIMES. "Will delight the amateur gardener, and indeed everyone else," SATURDAY REVIEW. Translated by M. and R. Weatherall. 59 illustrations. 159pp. 4½ x 6½.
T1014 Paperbound **$1.00**

THE ADVANCE OF THE FUNGI, E. C. Large. The dramatic story of the battle against fungi, from the year the potato blight hit Europe (1845) to 1940, and of men who fought and won it: Pasteur, Anton de Bary, Tulasne, Berkeley, Woronin, Jensen, many others. Combines remarkable grasp of facts and their significance with skill to write dramatic, exciting prose. "Philosophically witty, fundamentally thoughtful, always mature," NEW YORK HERALD TRIBUNE. "Highly entertaining, intelligent, penetrating," NEW YORKER. Bibliography. 64 illustrations. 6 full-page plates. 488pp. 5⅜ x 8½.
T437 Paperbound **$2.25**

THE PAINTER'S METHODS AND MATERIALS, A. P. Laurie. Adviser to the British Royal Academy discusses the ills that paint is heir to and the methods most likely to counteract them. Examining 48 masterpieces by Fra Lippo Lippi, Millais, Boucher, Rembrandt, Romney, Van Eyck, Velazquez, Michaelangelo, Botticelli, Frans Hals, Turner, and others, he tries to discover how special and unique effects were achieved. Not conjectural information, but certain and authoritative. Beautiful, sharp reproductions, plus textual illustrations of apparatus and the results of experiments with pigments and media. 63 illustrations and diagrams. Index. 250pp. 5⅜ x 8.
T1019 Clothbound **$3.75**

CATALOGUE OF DOVER BOOKS

GEOMETRY OF FOUR DIMENSIONS, H. P. Manning. Unique in English as a clear, concise introduction to this fascinating subject. Treatment is primarily synthetic and Euclidean, although hyperplanes and hyperspheres at infinity are considered by non-Euclidean forms. Historical introduction and foundations of 4-dimensional geometry; perpendicularity; simple angles; angles of planes; higher order; symmetry; order, motion; hyperpyramids, hypercones, hyperspheres; figures with parallel elements; volume, hypervolume in space; regular polyhedroids. Glossary of terms. 74 illustrations. ix + 348pp. 5⅜ x 8.　　　　　　　S182 Paperbound **$2.00**

PAPER FOLDING FOR BEGINNERS, W. D. Murray and F. J. Rigney. A delightful introduction to the varied and entertaining Japanese art of origami (paper folding), with a full, crystal-clear text that anticipates every difficulty; over 275 clearly labeled diagrams of all important stages in creation. You get results at each stage, since complex figures are logically developed from simpler ones. 43 different pieces are explained: sailboats, frogs, roosters, etc. 6 photographic plates. 279 diagrams. 95pp. 5⅝ x 8⅜.　　　　　　　T713 Paperbound **$1.00**

SATELLITES AND SCIENTIFIC RESEARCH, D. King-Hele. An up-to-the-minute non-technical account of the man-made satellites and the discoveries they have yielded up to September of 1961. Brings together information hitherto published only in hard-to-get scientific journals. Includes the life history of a typical satellite, methods of tracking, new information on the shape of the earth, zones of radiation, etc. Over 60 diagrams and 6 photographs. Mathematical appendix. Bibliography of over 100 items. Index. xii + 180pp. 5⅜ x 8½.
　　　　　　　T703 Paperbound **$2.00**

LOUIS PASTEUR, S. J. Holmes. A brief, very clear, and warmly understanding biography of the great French scientist by a former Professor of Zoology in the University of California. Traces his home life, the fortunate effects of his education, his early researches and first theses, and his constant struggle with superstition and institutionalism in his work on microorganisms, fermentation, anthrax, rabies, etc. New preface by the author. 159pp. 5⅜ x 8.
　　　　　　　T197 Paperbound **$1.00**

THE ENJOYMENT OF CHESS PROBLEMS, K. S. Howard. A classic treatise on this minor art by an internationally recognized authority that gives a basic knowledge of terms and themes for the everyday chess player as well as the problem fan: 7 chapters on the two-mover; 7 more on 3- and 4-move problems; a chapter on selfmates; and much more. "The most important one-volume contribution originating solely in the U.S.A.," Alain White. 200 diagrams. Index. Solutions. viii + 212pp. 5⅜ x 8.　　　　　　　T742 Paperbound **$1.25**

SAM LOYD AND HIS CHESS PROBLEMS, Alain C. White. Loyd was (for all practical purposes) the father of the American chess problem and his protégé and successor presents here the diamonds of his production, chess problems embodying a whimsy and bizarre fancy entirely unique. More than 725 in all, ranging from two-move to extremely elaborate five-movers, including Loyd's contributions to chess oddities—problems in which pieces are arranged to form initials, figures, other by-paths of chess problem found nowhere else. Classified according to major concept, with full text analyzing problems, containing selections from Loyd's own writings. A classic to challenge your ingenuity, increase your skill. Corrected republication of 1913 edition. Over 750 diagrams and illustrations. 744 problems with solutions. 471pp. 5⅜ x 8½.　　　　　　　T928 Paperbound **$2.25**

FABLES IN SLANG & MORE FABLES IN SLANG, George Ade. 2 complete books of major American humorist in pungent colloquial tradition of Twain, Billings. 1st reprinting in over 30 years includes "The Two Mandolin Players and the Willing Performer," "The Base Ball Fan Who Took the Only Known Cure," "The Slim Girl Who Tried to Keep a Date that was Never Made," 42 other tales of eccentric, perverse, but always funny characters. "Touch of genius," H. L. Mencken. New introduction by E. F. Bleiler. 86 illus. 208pp. 5⅜ x 8.
　　　　　　　T533 Paperbound **$1.00**

Prices subject to change without notice.

Dover publishes books on art, music, philosophy, literature, languages, history, social sciences, psychology, handcrafts, orientalia, puzzles and entertainments, chess, pets and gardens, books explaining science, intermediate and higher mathematics, mathematical physics, engineering, biological sciences, earth sciences, classics of science, etc. Write to:

　　　　　　　Dept. catrr.
　　　　　　　Dover Publications, Inc.
　　　　　　　180 Varick Street, N. Y. 14, N. Y.